La Posada

Short Stories of an Inn

by
Maria Emilia Ortega-Samper

La Posada

Short Stories of an Inn

by
Maria Emilia Ortega-Samper

Published by PenCraft Publishing

PenCraft Publishing

La Posada: short stories from an Inn

La Posada: short stories from an Inn

ISBN: (Kindle) 978-1-939556-42-4
ISBN: (Print)   978-1-939556-41-7

First published: September 2018 UK

Edited by: Barbara J Cormack (PenCraft Publishing)
Front cover image by: Teresa Mariño
Internal images by: Sergio Perez

Published by: PenCraft Publishing
a division of PenCraft Books Limited,
27 Old Gloucester Street, London, WC1N 3AX, UK

www.PenCraftPublishing.com

La Posada: short stories from an Inn

Acknowledgements

I would like to thank many amazing people, who have made possible my journey writing this book:

First and foremost, Barbara J Cormack and PenCraft Books, who encouraged and helped me throughout this project;

Mateo Samper, who gave me a light as to how I should write it. His wonderful ideas made my stories better;

Teresa Mariño, my artist friend, who made a beautiful cover for the book;

Sergio Perez, who helped me with the incredible drawing that portrays the inn as I envisioned it;

Lina Samper, who took my picture for the cover;

Catalina Mejia, who contributed with ideas and helped in my writing; and

My family and most especially my sisters Carmen, Camila and Rosario, who have been by my side during this experience.

La Posada: short stories from an Inn

Dedication

To my dear friend Andres, who moved by my stories continuously challenged me to write them.

To my Mom, who wanted to be my first reader but passed away before I could finish it. I promise to read it out loud, so you can hear every word.

La Posada: short stories from an Inn

Welcome to La Posada

La Posada

La Posada: short stories from an Inn

Contents

La Posada: short stories from an Inn

Intrigue

La Posada

La Posada: short stories from an Inn

I grew up hearing my parents and grandparents telling me stories that mesmerized me with their perpetually happy endings. At bedtime, my sisters and I would doze off with my father's stories about The Phantom, a hero for us. Every night The Phantom saved someone in a mysterious land called Rangoon, and continue to do so endlessly. He was a cartoon character during the 60's, portrayed as a man in a grey suit and mask, who suddenly appeared when there were people in distress. It was a mystery where he came from, and where he'd go after succeeding in his feat.

Each night we expected new adventure from this hero; who surpassed all our imaginations. The most wonderful thing is that every night my Dad had something new to tell us; his imagination was infinite and that provoked absolute fascination in me.

As I grew older, I played a game when I was outdoors with my grandfather. He would challenge me to imagine the life of a stranger from their perspective. He would pick someone at random and would ask me to tell him this person's story. This contributed to my curiosity about the people around me; and made me wonder about the lives of others.

I wanted to imagine that they all had happy lives full of hope. It hurt me when I met people who were experiencing difficulties. Their pain sparked a mission: I would help those around me for as long as I could. However, as time went by I also began to realize that in the real world, while some stories end well, others end tragically; but what I am sure of is that there is nothing sadder than being indifferent to the events surrounding us.

When I then had the opportunity to work in a small Inn in the city, I encountered many stories in which the people involved required help. I could only observe from a distance, and although in many instances they asked for help, on several occasions it was not possible.

From its inauguration the Inn was located in a large house, built in the 20th century in a gorgeous English Neighborhood in the north of the city of Bogotá, Colombia. Pastel color walls gave it a warm atmosphere during our cold nights. It also had a quaint courtyard and eleven rooms filled with leisurely beds yawning in anticipation of the weary tenants. Designed to appeal to travelers who wanted reasonably priced accommodation in an ideal location not far away from the historical center and Zona Rosa; the Inn would attract young travelers who wanted to visit museums and historical venues during the day, and bars or nice restaurants at night.

Two areas of our Inn were essential for our travelers. The first was the living room; designed as a meeting place for our guests. They met around a television set that always had the travelers watching the same news and soap operas, resulting in endless conversations about what they were watching. The second was the courtyard; a place where 4 park benches gave those travelers interested in discussing their latest sightseeing visits or trekking experiences the opportunity to do so, while sipping a nice hot cup of complimentary Colombian coffee.

Our mission was to make the travelers feel like guests in our home, by creating and maintaining a cozy family atmosphere. Throughout the years we had two types of guests, and we referred to them as the passengers and the regulars. The passengers were the ones who stayed without requiring much; they were distant and reserved, unlike the regulars, who always found a way to make us part of their lives. The regulars were impossible not to befriend because they needed or wanted to share their stories with us. In the following chapters I will only mention those stories that throughout the years I was at the Inn, for one reason or another, had a great impact on me. Some of the guests came back, but some of them just appeared as a chapter in our lives and left never to return. The mixture of emotions they all left feels like a laundry basket, where you can find either your favorite red dress or your old holed socks. These are their stories.

La Posada: short stories from an Inn

From Italy

La Posada: short stories from an Inn

It was a rainy day and with a higher occupation than usual at the Inn, the only available rooms had a shared bathroom. This type of room is very common in Europe; therefore, when this gentleman arrived from Italy I was not worried. Gino seemed deeply troubled and arrived accompanied by a group of men who appeared foreign and clearly worried about him. His face conveyed a somber attitude.

Gino was in his late 30's or early 40's; tall and handsome with curly silver plaited hair. He looked European and his face reflected disillusionment and sadness. When he arrived, my first thought was that he had some sort of legal problem, as the gentlemen who accompanied him were Embassy officials. We were inquisitive; especially when one of the Embassy officials came into my office and explained: "I need a room where Gino can stay because he has to stay for several days in the country".

No problem I thought to myself; room 209 was perfect for him. It was small and a warm cozy room for our cold nights. Since the Inn opened, this room had become a preferred room for guests with extended stays. It had no private bathroom but as I imagined, for Gino this was not a problem. We left the front desk and before taking him to the room, I gave him a tour of the facilities. He followed me like a **shadow**, without uttering a word or looking very interested, just being polite. After showing him to his room, he returned to speak to his companions for a while in the living room; apparently receiving his instructions. After accompanying them to the door, Gino returned to his room.

The next day, towards mid-morning, he came down for breakfast. Once he had finished eating, he looked a bit lost.

"Can I help you with something?" I inquired politely.

"I need to know where I can receive an urgent fax from Italy." he responded solemnly.

I gave him the guests' card with our Inn information - the address, email, and fax and phone numbers. Gino left in a hurry and within a half an hour, we received a fax of approximately twelve pages. They contained court documents from Italy; documenting that someone was being tried for child kidnapping. When he returned, he received the fax with apprehension.

"Thank you. Would you do me the favor and help me translate these documents?" he inquired. "I need to take them to a lawyer as quickly as possible."

Once I started to help him with the translation of the documents, I realized that the court proceedings were related to his wife. She had left Italy with their child and without Gino's permission. I decided not to ask for details. I thought he would explain the situation when he felt he could do so. Something that happened shortly afterwards.

For several days, he came and went; always traveling with the same people that had brought him to our Inn. Suddenly one day, Gino walked into my office extremely anxious:

"Six months ago I lost my daughter and my wife" he stated. "And the worst thing is that I don't know where they are."

I stared back, dumbfounded by the revelation and unable to utter any words, as I did not believe what he was telling me. For years I had heard similar stories, such as the American mother who visited Iran with her family and once there, the husband compelled her to stay in that country with their daughter. This woman was able to escape to Turkey and returned home to the United States safely. Her story became a movie soon afterwards; and this mother's courage provoked a sense of admiration with all the women that I knew. Unfortunately, this was not the only one; other similar experiences were widely published in books and movies. Every time, I read something of this nature, I was relieved that it had not happened to anyone close to me, until now.

Gino's story began inconspicuously enough: he worked for an Italian engineering company that was building an important hydroelectric project in Colombia. As one of the engineers on this construction job site, he lived in our country for several years. While here (in Colombia), he met a young woman and fell madly in love with her. After a year they decided to marry, and lived a normal happy life enjoying being newlyweds. At the end of the contract in Colombia, the Italian company returned its employees to Italy. At this point, nothing seemed to anticipate what was going to happen next. Gino was delighted that they were moving to his country, and had great hopes of his new married life. But, after a few months, his wife became weary and unable to adjust being so far from her family.

Although he tried to make things easier, nothing seemed to satisfy her. Gino changed jobs; looking for a better work schedule that would help with their relationship. It helped initially because his wife became pregnant. Nine months later a beautiful baby girl was born and they called her Maria. Since her birth, Gino thought of this child as a gift from heaven; his wife finally seemed happy. Two years went by and she stopped mentioning her intention to return to Colombia. Life seemed happier and under control, until the day his wife received news from home. This news made her smile; her brother was planning to visit them... Obviously, considering how thrilled his wife was with this news, Gino was complacent. Gino was hopeful this visit would bring her peace with her marriage and living so far away from home. Unfortunately for Gino it was wishful thinking, as things were about to change drastically.

During her brother's visit, she became aggressive and condescending. Once again asking if she could return to Colombia with their daughter for a while. Obviously Gino loved his family and didn't want to be left alone, even for a fairly short time; so he was not interested. Not interested at all. The situation continued being very complicated and Gino asked a friend for advice. His friend urged him to consult with a lawyer to prevent any problem; and with the advice of several lawyers, he introduced a preventive measure to stop his child leaving the country without his written consent.

But soon the day came when all his fears came true. He returned home from work and found the house empty.

"They should be taking a walk and will be back shortly", Gino thought.

But as the minutes became hours, racked with concern Gino went to the police. A couple of days later received the news: it had been established that they could have left the country. Definitely not through any Italian port, but there was a strong possibility they took a bus and headed for Germany. From Germany they were able to take a plane back to Colombia.

Months passed without news of his wife and child. Desperate, he boarded a plane to Colombia to search for them. He remembered his mother-in-law's address, and upon arriving at the house found it empty. He was consumed with a terrible disappointment. His despair was overwhelming because he was not sure how or where to find them. At this time, the city of Bogotá was a city of seven million people, and there was no organization that would enable him to find them easily. He was determined to find his wife and child. After some research through relatives and acquaintances, Gino got a lead. He was not sure how his friend got the information, but it was good enough for him. Gino camped out for hours next to the apartment address he was given. Suddenly, in the middle of the afternoon, a taxi arrived with a woman and a little girl as passengers. His heart was pounding so much with the anguish that he thought he was suffering a heart attack. When the passengers got out of the taxi, he was able to confirm what he suspected for so many months: his wife and daughter had fled to Bogota, and now, they were just a few meters away from him.

Remembering the instructions received from his lawyer, Gino did not make his presence known. The lawyer needed to include his wife's address in the complaint presented to the relevant official agency. This complaint would recognize his claim to visitation rights. For this reason, he should not let his wife know he was in the country looking for them. If he did, he could risk the chance to losing them again. He went straight to the lawyer's office to provide him this information. The complaint was filed before the relevant official agency in charge of protecting children in Colombia; Bienestar Familiar, and it included the documentation sent by the courts of Italy. He was confident because the lawyers told him the law was on his side, and in a few days could return to see his daughter again.

Indeed a few days later, the official document arrived granting him the rights to visit the child. Initially, this had to be done under the mother's supervision, but he did not care. The moment Gino knew that he was about to hold his daughter in his arms, he became another person; he kept smiling, shaking his head incredulously and in traditional Italian fashion, embraced us all warmly whenever he saw us.

This situation enraged Gino's wife. I could hear her shouting down the phone at Gino from my post at the front desk. I watched helplessly as Gino squirmed through her tirades; but try as she might to dissuade him from visiting, Gino, after crossing an ocean and combing a major city to find his daughter, would not be denied his right to visit.

"There is no way," Gino declared calmly, "I've waited for this opportunity for too long and I don't want to wait a minute more."

That same afternoon, a very excited Gino left for the visit armed with a bundle of new toys. We all wished him luck.

As we all went about our business that day, folding the linens, booking reservations, cutting fresh fruit for the mid afternoon snack break, our thoughts drifted back to Gino and his climactic meeting. Each time the front door opened, my eyes shot towards it with anticipation; seeking Gino's smile. To no avail.

But Gino's smile didn't return. He slipped back in late at night, shoulders hunched, his toy arsenal depleted. The visit had been made under the strict supervision of his wife and this sapped his ability to enjoy time with his daughter, Maria. He wanted to recover all those months that he had lost, and eliminate the lingering fear that she might forget how much he loved her. Fortunately, his daughter recognized him immediately and Gino was able to enjoy her company. That was until his wife considered that the visit had been sufficiently long enough, but for Gino it wasn't long enough. However, he had found Maria and was not going to allow anyone to take her away from him again.

This happiness was short lived. Whenever he wanted to see Maria and called his wife, she responded that it was not possible due to one excuse or other; "the girl is sick" or "the girl has to go to the doctor" or "the girl is not in". He decided to pay a concierge, who worked close by in a neighboring building, to provide him with information as to his daughter's movements – was she at home or not? Every day, he would call the doorman in the afternoon, just after Maria returned from daycare. If she was home, despite his wife's reluctance, Gino would visit her. His wife was always able to make the visits shorter and shorter. It was then when Gino started to become really frustrated with the State agencies.

Gino considered his lawyer incompetent. The lawyer was not able to get authorizations from his wife to anything he proposed. He was not interested in taking his child away from her mother, but he wanted to claim his rights to be the best father possible. Gino tried to promote a truce between him and his wife; programming trips for his daughter during vacation periods, but he got nowhere. It seemed no-one could guarantee the only thing he wanted the most in this world and that was to be the father of his child. In addition, money was becoming scarce. Between the hotel bill and the lawyer's fees, Gino's bank account was drying up. He was forced to return to work in Italy. With great sadness, he left Colombia to return his country with more fear than happiness; but with the hope of seeing his daughter again.

He returned to Colombia in the next two years. But during these trips, the visits become more frustrating. The government agencies were very slow deciding his case. He petitioned for unlimited visitation rights while he was here in Colombia: yet, the family court hearings took too much time progressing and judging his request. Added to which, there was always something or someone sabotaging the allowed visits he had with his child.

Fortunately, at the end of the third year, Gino was authorized to take Maria to the Inn for his visits, but had to return her to his wife's house by the end of the afternoon.

His visits however, continued to be full of frustrations. He requested permission to bring his daughter back to Italy during her holidays. Even though there was an invitation for a member of his wife's family to accompany his daughter, his wife's lawyer would not allow it. His wife was unable to return to Italy because of legal issues; as she had been tried for child abduction and the sentence remained in place at that point in time. However, the request presented to the Colombian courts was denied to him again and again by his wife's lawyer.

During the third year, Gino arrived with Claudia, his girlfriend. She was 30-years-old, also Italian, attractive and very friendly. She was Gino's moral support in his daily endeavors regarding Maria; visiting the lawyer, going with him to see his child, and basically becoming a booster for Gino's sometimes weakened spirit. It gave me the opportunity to suggest to him that having met someone special he could have a new life and visit his daughter every year. It would avoid so much suffering. Gino did not say a word or nod; he was simply silent, meditating on how incompressible this situation was. When his time came to leave, as always he would thank me for taking the time to help him; or just being there to hear him out. He simply didn't feel adequate; he felt tired with all the red tape he encountered. But despite it all, Gino hoped for a prompt return.

One year later, as I was organizing our reservations book in the front desk, Ricardo, our puzzled receptionist, said out loud: "Are you aware that Mr. Gino did not visit us this year?" I agreed but told him: "It would not surprise me that after all those years coming to visit, now he has friends where he can stay at for free". A situation that was not at all unusual for people who frequently travel to the same place; they end up making friends and are often able to stay with the friends which saves them from paying hotels.

We had not yet ended this conversation when sure enough through the front desk window, we saw a radiant Gino, accompanied by his daughter, walking towards our door. Ricardo and I were so astonished to see him with the girl that we ran to open the door and received him with a boisterous Italian-style welcome. I had so many questions that I didn't know when to start. I didn't have to wait long; Gino told us, "The truth is that in this instance my daughter´s mother urged me to come and visit Maria because she was very depressed."

He also mentioned that he had legally divorced the mother of his child. But, such was his ex-wife's concern over the health of their daughter that his ex-wife had gone to meet him on his arrival at the airport. Apparently the girl had lost weight, cried permanently and was falling behind in school. After several consultations with the Doctor his ex-wife found out that Maria wanted to see her dad. The Doctor recommended that Gino should visit urgently. Gino explained that he was not staying at the Inn because he was staying with some friends; however, he needed to need to reserve a couple of days at the Inn as his friends were traveling out of the country at the end of week.

"Is it too late to make a reservation for next Saturday?" he asked shyly.

"You know this is your home and you can come whenever you want". I said.

The following Saturday he arrived with a small bag. Unintentionally, I was alone at the front desk and proceeded to register him. He gave me his passport with a red cover; the same one he used when he came for the first time all those years ago. While reviewing the details of his passport as part of the check-in process, I opened it to the last page where his daughter was registered.

"Wow, how big is she now"? I asked, but he did not utter a word.

While doing the registration I remembered that, when he made the reservation, he mentioned that he had brought two suitcases.

"Is someone bringing the suitcases?"

He replied harshly: "Don't worry about them".

I was surprised because his demeanor had changed in only a few days. I attributed his annoyance to all the events that had happened to him in our country during the past few years. Once he had successfully checked-in, he went to his room.

He spent the weekend visiting his daughter.

On Monday around 11 o'clock in the morning his lawyer's secretary arrived. They were in the living room and as I was passing, he stopped me and with irritation in his voice told me: "Ms. Maria, I will never return to this country".

Once again, they denied his requests and had not met all the promises that were made.

"Have patience, you have won a lot of ground." I said reassuringly.

He just did not care. This time, his look was different; his eyes expressed frustration and anger. Nothing I could say to him would make a difference and it was easy to understand why. It seemed unbelievable that his ex-wife was not able to see the great love this man had for his daughter; how was it was possible that she could be so selfish as to prevent him from being part of their child's life... In the end, nothing foresaw the drama that was about to unfold.

The next day; it was Tuesday, December 5 at 11 o'clock; I received a call on my home phone from Jose, the night receptionist.

"The Gaula (the police anti-kidnapping in Colombia) are here looking for Mr. Gino, but I did not let them in".

What?! I thought.

I did not understand anything he was trying to explain over

the telephone. According to the police, there was a serious suggestion that Gino had vanished with his daughter.

Jose reassured me it was not possible, as he said: "This must be a mistake, he was not able to leave the country because I already checked his room and I have found his Passport."

The Gaula agents were relieved, but the lead officer explained that they would be returning the next day. I was very tired: we were at full occupancy at the Inn and we were taking care of fifteen additional guests.

"Is my presence at the Inn necessary?" I asked Jose.

"The passport was in his room therefore; Gino is unable to leave the country." he responded.

The next day dawned clear with very blue and bright skies. It was a typical morning in December, and while I was on my way to the Inn, I kept thinking about the Gino incident. I was hoping it had been resolved and that Maria (Gino's daughter) had finally returned home. For obvious reasons, I arrived that morning earlier than normal but it was only at 9 a.m. that a captain of the Gaula showed up. He confirmed what José and my employees had already told me. Gino picked his daughter up at school that day before 3 p.m. but never arrived at 5:30 p.m.; the hour he had agreed to return her to her mother. The captain kindly requested that I accompany him to check the room. Obviously, I agreed and went with him to search room 101. I felt the anguish difficult to describe. All kinds of thoughts went through my head. I thought perhaps this is just a terrible mistake, and Gino was out somewhere with some friends and he would show up with his daughter at any time. At that moment, I was trying to think positively that what I was told happened the day before, wasn't true; but when I opened the closet my fears returned. There was the passport with dark covers that José had found the night before.

At that precise moment, I realized something wrong. With reluctance, I turned around to give the captain the terrible news, when he saw the passport and said with relief, "Good, he has been unable to leave the country because he left his Passport".

I was speechless but had to give him the dreadful news, "I have to inform you that this Passport is new and Gino has another Passport, which is also valid". The captain was stunned.

The captain looked at me in disbelief, and I explained that when Gino checked-in a few days earlier, he presented me with another Passport; one that had a red cover. We quickly returned to the front desk to verify the Passport information recorded in the Aliens National Registry, a book in which all foreign visitors must be recorded in when they register for accommodation. As I expected, the numbers of both passports were different. We returned to the room and as I opened the closet, deep into the second section, we found that Gino had left, strategically placed on top of a sheet of paper, monies to pay Gino's hotel bill with us. In his own handwriting, he paid up for 3 nights plus a couple of sodas. In addition, he left a small box of chocolates that made me angry. Even though it was his way of thanking us I guess; I felt it was unacceptable from every point of view.

For obvious reasons, the girl's mother created a great scandal in newspapers and on the radio stations. One of the latter called us asking for details; and the distraught mother wanted to know if there was something new or if by chance he had contacted us, but nothing ... he just disappeared.

A completely unjustified action. Since her mother (Gino's ex-wife) could not travel to Italy, the only one who lost out with this incident was their daughter. This action seemed to be premeditated.

After pondering this for several hours; and with the other employees, debating where he had gone, we recalled several circumstances that made us think that he gone to Panama. The stay at the Inn was a screen because he never brought with him the two suitcases he said he had brought from Italy. There was the question as to what happened to them? Who had them? On the day he checked-in at the Inn, he only had a small bag with old clothes, which he left behind. Was someone else helping him? Things that happened previously made us think that he began to create this plan from September. I remembered what I told him the weekend he registered;

"In the month of September we received several emails from your friend Nero asking if everything was going well".

Gino blushed and said, "He made a mistake because I was working in Panama".

Although I was surprised by his reaction, my only thought was that he had come to our country, but stayed somewhere else and was embarrassed by it. At the time, it never occurred to me that something like this would transpire.

Despite everything he went through with his child, all of us at the Inn felt betrayed because we believed in him. In our

22

wildest dreams we never imagined that he would put us in such predicament. But on the other hand, after being witnesses to his years of frustration, it is understandable that it happened solely out of desperation.

We never received news about or from him or news about the girl's whereabouts. It was definitely a sad episode. This child should not have been part of that dispute and I believe it will be difficult for both parents explain to their daughter why they took such terrible decisions. Hopefully, they have reconciled their differences and the girl has been returned to her mother where she belongs, and may her father be part of her life as he deserves.

La Posada: short stories from an Inn

.

Heart-breaking Stories

La Posada

3

La Posada: short stories from an Inn

The following are three stories of kindness and courage which stay close to my heart. They relate to youngsters facing tough situations in their young lives, and who faced these situations with extraordinary courage.

JOHNNY

The first story is about **Johnny.** He called from Australia to make the room reservation. The telephone connection was bad and I could not really understand what he was saying. I was only able to understand the dates he planned to be in Bogotá. He told me that he was looking for someone, but on the call, I was unable to understand most of what he tried to say.

Sure enough, a few days later he arrived in a taxi. He was a young man, about 18 years old, with Latin features and his nerves showed his inexperience in this type of venture. Although Johnny knew some Spanish, he was relieved when he learned that we could speak in English. While he registered at the front desk, he began to tell me his story. I was deeply touched as he went into the details.

He was the eldest of several children and was able to recall small things happening to them ten years ago. He remembered terrible moments, where they all felt hungry, cold and no-one showing them love. He had vague memories of something tragic happening to their parents but had no details or memory of this event. As an eight-year-old, he did not understand why in an instance, he, his two brothers and a sister ended up being placed for adoption in a place he remembered as *Casita de Maria*. Fortunately for him, after a short period of time he and his two brothers were adopted by an Italian couple. However, despite this new beginning for them, something tortured the siblings; they all remembered a baby sister being separated from them when they were adopted. They never saw her again.

Once the adoption process was finalized, Johnny and his brothers left for Italy with their new parents. Shortly afterwards the new family decided to emigrate to and live in Australia; a country where they grew up and spent most of their lives since leaving Colombia. The memory of their sister always remained with them and the three boys continually thought about her. So much so, that when once the brothers reached their legal age allowing them to begin to work in Sydney, they decided that they needed to reach a goal which would allow them to find their sister – eight thousand dollars. The most endearing thing about this amount, was that no one advised them about this specific figure; they simply considered this was what they needed in order to search for her in Colombia.

Johnny was chosen to make the trip and all the necessary inquiries; not only because he was the eldest but also he was the one with more memories. He had a vague memory of the adoption process, only recalling a small number of things. He recalled some names but was not sure if they were related to his search or not. Fortunately, our conversation was made in private because I was afraid that with Johnny's ingenuity and enthusiasm, he may attract the interest of someone strange, and could end losing the money they all worked so hard for.

It touched me; the pride displayed by him when he explained the purpose of their mission, as well as their work done by all the siblings in order to find their sister. When he finished his story, I told him that would do my best to help him untangle what had happened. I really had high hopes to help him as I found the situation overwhelmingly fascinating.

To begin our quest, the details of the adoption were needed. This would help with the search of their missing sister. Of all the names, La Casita de Maria was the name Johnny clearly remembered and was our first clue. We began by trying to find its address on the internet and in the yellow pages' phone directory, but there was nothing even remotely similar. Johnny rushed to his room and brought me all the certificates he had. I started to read the documents and suddenly found something important: the adoption had only been done after the children's picture appeared on *El Tiempo*, one of the major newspapers in Colombia. The paper was dated ten years ago. Although Johnny did not have a copy of it, I remembered that I could ask for a duplicate. I contacted the paper's records department; the person in charge was very friendly and promised he could have a copy of the page the next day.

Johnny's eagerness was enormous. The next morning, I sent him, with someone we trusted to make sure he would not get lost, to pick up the copy of the picture. When he arrived back from the newspaper, Johnny showed us the photo of several children searching for their parents with the following: "for more information go to La Casita de Maria". The address displayed is in a neighborhood of Bogotá called Egypt. Johnny pointed out all his siblings including a small baby (his sister). I then understood about his impatience to know what had happened to their sister. It was late in the afternoon and I told him that it was not a good hour of the day to venture into that part of town especially as he didn't speak Spanish very well. In addition to which, it was important that he could go with someone who could help him find an answer to all his queries. As it was his first trip away from home and he barely speak or understand our language, he accepted my suggestion.

The next day I called a cab that worked for our guests. I asked the driver not only to take him to the adoption house but also to wait for him. I advised Johnny to take the picture from the newspaper. He left worried, but interested to know about her. Fortunately, he returned in the afternoon radiating relief and happiness.

I have always believed that some things happen for a reason, and this story is one of them. It was by chance, that when they arrived at the adoption house, none other than the person who was the Director of La Casita de Maria when they were handed over to family welfare, was there. Although this man was not in charge of this adoption house any more, he still worked for them. It seemed predestined. Johnny remembered the Director fondly, as he never allowed them to feel abandoned. Rather he became their guardian until the day the Italian couple adopted the three boys. Johnny timidly asked the Director if he remembered him, and his "of course" answer was a great relief.

When the Director gave Johnny details on their adoption process, he explained that it had been very difficult to find a couple that would adopt the four of them. Very few children had the luck of being adopted together. More so in their case, where they were three little boys.

Johnny told him that their adoptive parents, the Tonelli's, had not been the best parents because they were so strict, that as soon as he could, he decided to live on his own.

30

The Director of La Casita de Maria replied immediately: "you're more fortunate than you think because you would not have had a future if all of you remained in the conditions you were in."

He proceeded to describe details Johnny did not know about his family. The details related to his main concern was answered; they had a sister who was adopted by a couple residing in Paris. He would try to communicate with their sister's adoptive parents to find out if they authorized him to contact her; because her sister was only 10 years old. Once he had the approval, he would give Johnny the information on how to find her in France.

The Director gave Johnny a brief account of their biological parents' history. Because of the terrible events, he did not delve into details. However, Johnny did want to know about their fate. The Director explained that his mother had been murdered by his father and that he was serving a jail sentence of several years. Since the closest family member was their grandmother, the children were handed over to her. However, as she faced economic challenges, she decided to hand them over to family welfare.

Despite this painful news, Johnny wanted to verify everything. In discussion with the Director, it was decided that the Director would help him make arrangements to find his grandmother. At his young age, he was about to encounter a painful and depressing situation. Unable to fully grasp what he saw; an old woman living in a run-down cottage with cardboard and tin tiles in absolute misery; he understood his grandmother's decision to provide a better future for him, his brothers, and his sister. This sight was what most shocked him. Because of this decision, their lives took a huge turn for the better; and it did happen. All the boys finished higher education, they were bilingual, and had something to eat every day. Something totally unthinkable in their grandmother's position. Finding out was not a relief because he was shocked to see how his biological family lived in real life.

That afternoon Johnny came to my office with the Director of La Casita of Maria to say farewell. He was so emotional that he could hardly speak; his goodbye was whispered. Before returning to his home, he had made a decision to help his grandmother. We got the impression that the Director was ready to help him with this task. I was glad, because he looked like a good person and was clearly happy to see Johnny again. To make things easier, the Director had offered Johnny accommodation in his home.

Johnny came to find his sister. Although he could not find her in our country (Colombia), he was advised on the many possibilities there are in France. There are many programs uniting adopted children with their biological mothers. Instead, he was going to help his grandmother, who, thanks to her foresight, had given all the siblings a better life.

MARK

Our second case was **Mark**. Mark was adopted by a Dutch couple and who did not speak a word of Spanish. Mark has Latino features; he is mixed-race and not very tall, with dark hair and brown eyes. It was a great contrast to his father's Nordic traits. He was adopted when he was a month old and was privileged to have parents, who always showed him lots of love. When he was old enough they told him about his adoption reassuring him that he had been the best gift for their family. However, as he grew old, he began to have concerns about his origin. Therefore, the adoptive parents began to find a way to contact the biological mother as it was noticeable that Mark and his adoptive parents had a very special relationship.

His adoption was done through a prestigious private institution in Bogotá. The adopting parents requested information about his biological mother but, according to this institution, there were no records about her. Fortunately, years later a program seeking the reuniting of adopted children with their biological mothers created in The Netherlands was able to do so and the information they were seeking, was finally made available. The report explained that Mark's biological mother gave him because of her extreme financial situation. When she fell pregnant, she was already a mother of three small children and barely survived. The thought of having one more mouth to feed really worried her. In her anguish at the hospital a social worker approached her and, knowing her living conditions, explained to the biological mother that there was the possibility of putting the baby up for adoption. The worker, understanding the situation, suggested this solution knowing that this child could have a better life. While Mark's biological mother didn't hesitate a moment, although she dreamed of seeing him again.

Once the adoption was completed, the biological mother was told that her baby had been adopted by a couple from The Netherlands. Not knowing where The Netherlands was, she asked one of her other children if he could show her where this country was located on the map.

When she met Mark, she told him it had become an obsession to see again him. A long time passed before she got any news from her son; but one day, many years later, she received the call she had been waiting for. He had found her and wanted to meet her. She could not believe it and eagerly awaited that day.

The first time he arrived with his parents, he was thrilled to meet his biological mother; but they were overwhelmed with the living situation and the shortages of his new found relatives. They met at his biological mother's house in Ciudad Bolivar, one of the poorest neighborhoods of the city, and the shortage of basic necessities surprised them all. Mark then knew how fortunate he was; not only because he had a very good life without financial and shortage problems, additionally he was in school and about to receive a rent free apartment from the Dutch government. In this young man's mind, he could not understand why his mother lived in such poverty.

He asked his parents for help; and for years they sent money so she could improve her situation and move forward. The biological mother was able to sew and all she needed was a sewing machine. They sent her the necessary monies to buy a good machine that would enable her to earn enough for her and the other siblings.

With the help of his adoptive parents, Mark gave her a machine. This meant that she could find work and improve her conditions and those of his siblings.

In the year we met him, Mark had lost his adopted mother to a battle against cancer. Though both Mark and his father had not recovered from their loss; they decided to come to visit his Colombian family. Both were very happy to find them in better conditions. Mark's father told me that it was a pleasure to see them well dressed and more especially, healthy. With their help, the biological mother with her sewing workshop was successful; which improved their finances and their standard of living.

Mark thanked us for our hospitality and told us would not be able to return for a long time, as he would be marrying soon and finishing his college studies. He said he would keep in contact and was flying back home with the serenity of seeing his relatives in better circumstances.

THE CHILDREN OF THE WAR

The third case was the most endearing. Informally they were called **the children of the war**; a name used by the officials from the Ministry of Culture. This name described the children were selected to participate in a program from the Children Division. Annually, they chose a very select group of children coming from the so-called red zones of Mapiripan, Montes de Maria, San José del Guaviare and the region of Catatumbo.

Annually officials from the Children's Division of the Ministry of Culture and UNICEF sought to give recognition to a number of children to reward their courage. These officials worked hard throughout the year at a regional level, to help these kids survive in these violent surroundings. These children lived in permanent danger from the bullets of armed groups. So, towards the end of the year, they chose a group of children who had somehow excelled in their communities, and brought them initially to Bogotá (the capital). They organized a range of different plans, including visits to museums and landmarks so they could get a better understanding the history of our country. After a few days exploring Bogotá, the group traveled to Cartagena so they could enjoy the sea. We were lucky, as our Inn was chosen to accommodate these children. We provided the children with a family oriented environment, and when they arrived we greeted them with great affection.

In the same year, two children in this group touched my soul; a boy from the Guaviare region and a small girl from Mapiripan. They will both remain in my memory forever.

Twelve-year-old **Gabriel** arrived from a rural county in the Guaviare region. As soon as he arrived at the Inn, he immediately started to search for the exchange library. This type of library serves guests who can choose one book to read but must leave a different book on the bookshelf. In this way, our guests can find books on all subjects even though many look used as these books travel in backpacks or suitcases for months. However, it is an interesting way to exchange reading material because it allows a rotation of books for those guests who spend months traveling. With the exchange library they get something new to read.

It was fascinating watching Gabriel search because when he found the library, he was hypnotized by the sight of the books. I watched Gabriel to see if he was able to find something interesting, but after a while he said sadly: "nothing in Spanish".

Unfortunately, it was true. There were all sorts of English novels but nothing exciting in our language. The few books he found in Spanish included philosophy and mystery books, topics in which he showed no interest. His face expressed his disappointment, so much so that I thought I should do something about it. This child had enough challenges with the environment in which they lived, that I felt that he deserved something pleasant. Guerrilla and paramilitary continually fought in their region; in many instances making life absolutely frightening; but despite this daily danger, Gabriel always attended his rural school. This was a school with few students, who arrived in many unconventional ways including by canoe, to attend their lessons. However, the teachers told me that he was an excellent student and an avid reader. They had given me a detailed overview of the school and its lack of resources. Each teacher, using their own initiative, tried to give the students new material but it was not always financially feasible.

Then, I remembered that my mother had a library filled with a large number of children´s books that nobody read anymore. With her permission, I chose several titles that were of interest to me in my youth, and I thought they could be appealing to Gabriel. I was a little concerned by their condition, as the pages in many instances had turned a yellowish color. I tried to pick out those which were in the best possible shape. The next day, I arrived at the Inn with six books, and found him on the top of his bed reading a book which, according to Gabriel he was reading for the fifth time.

I left the books on his nightstand and told him: "They are yours so that you have something to read."

With his black and expressive eyes answered horrified: "But I am only going to be Bogota for three days, and I won't be able to read them even if I try."

I had no idea that the impact of a simple deed like this one would cause him anguish. His distress startled me and somehow I managed to tell him with a half-broken voice full of emotion: "These books are for you and you can take them back home".

He did not say a word. He did not seem to care that they were not new, something that surprised me. After browsing through each book, one by one; trying to read a little and understand the gift I had brought him, Gabriel went in search of his teacher. He showed her his 'new' books as he proudly called them.

Each day until the day he left, Gabriel did not stop thanking me. He was always giving me a description of how far his reading had progressed. For his first book, he had chosen Oliver Twist and had practically read the book in two days. I mentioned that if he continued to read this quickly, by the time he returned home he would not have anything to read.

With mischievous eyes told us: "Do not worry, I will read them again".

It was unbelievable that something so simple, could be so important in someone's life. I was glad to have be given this opportunity to provide him with new "treasures" and as of today I hope Gabriel´s wishes to have a better future have come true.

This story made my parents think that it didn't make any sense to have a library full of children's books when there were rural schools requiring reading material. After some research the entire library of children's books, was donated to two rural schools in the municipalities on the outskirts of Bogotá. There, we would have the confidence that the books would be put to good use instead of getting dusty in the basement of our house.

The second kid, **Martha** was a dramatic case. She arrived with a tangled and dirty long black hair, a flimsy dress and torn shoes. Officials from the Children´s Division believed she was eight years old but with her extensive malnutrition, they were not sure. She had been taken out from Mapiripan in a hurry because there was no time for any preparation.

Her parents were murdered and the Officials had to do something to help her. The night Martha arrived at the inn, she ate as if nobody had ever given her food in a while. This was with dire consequences as the meal caused her to vomit and gave her diarrhea; she quickly dehydrated. She was taken to the emergency room where, in addition to being fully diagnosed with extreme malnutrition, the medical staff decided to clean her. She had mud stuck to her skin and they had to wash her hair to remove head lice. None of this seemed the as bad as the fact that throughout this experience, she did not utter a single word. She did not answer questions and seemed to be living in her own world. Fortunately, one of the Officials had patience and treated her with affection. After a few hours, this gained her confidence and she was able to smile. Once she felt safe with them, Martha told her story.

A few days before, having lost the notion of time, it was on a date she could not remember, armed men arrived at their ranch where she lived with her parents, brothers and a blind grandfather. With a list in their hands, these men called her parents' names. Once they were identified, they were swiftly taken away from their house.

The grandfathers and grandsons fear was tremendous and they expected the worst. It happened! Martha's parents were murdered near where they lived. Martha didn't know who these men were and why they shot their parents. The children were left at the mercy of her blind grandfather. With a terrible fear that men could return; Martha, who was the eldest of the children, her grandfather and her brothers ran out of the house to hide in the forest.

From that fateful day they ate only raw vegetation because the children did not know how to light a fire, and the grandfather was unable to do so. Fortunately, after a few days they were rescued and safe. Her silence was the product of a terrible anguish for those who were left behind; she did not know what had happened with her grandfather and her brothers. After hearing the story, the social workers assured Martha that they would be in touch with those who handled her case in Mapiripan, so they could look after them.

A few days later, once Martha had recovered, she was able to participate in the planned activities and was happy to visit the sea. Her sullen look had changed a bit! When you consider all the suffering she had gone through at her young age, her uncertainties had been overwhelming. We knew that her return to their village would not be easy, but at least we had the confirmation that her grandfather and the other children were under the protection of the State, and they were going to have permanent counseling to take them forward.

Whenever the children of this program returned, we were filled with great satisfaction because, with courage, many of the children had managed to stop the war snatching their childhood away. This program was great and a real treat for all those brave boys and girls. Everyone, including the officials at the children's division, felt that we were lucky considering we only didn't live in the warzone and only heard about it in the news. When we learned what these kids lived through, it was very difficult to understand. All of us wanted an end to this conflict so that children can be children and experience a future in peace.

La Posada: short stories from an Inn

The Teams

La Posada: short stories from an Inn

Accommodating athletes was my passion. They do not have the same needs or concerns of a typical guest but are disciplined individuals requiring special care. Taking into account that I had relationships with several sports associations, we received various delegations from volleyball and soccer squads, track and field, to squash and cycling athletes. The athletes that stayed with us felt at home at the Inn, an effect that transcended into their sports performances.

I remember the Squash National Team that was going to compete in a tournament near Bogotá, and were scheduled to stay only one night at our Inn. Because the next day they would leave to stay at a hotel closer to the sports venue, but to my surprise were back the next day. The athletes missed our atmosphere and decided that it was preferable to travel every day a little more, that staying at a cold and unfriendly hotel.

SQUASH PLAYERS

Of all the delegations, our most frequent guests were the squash players. I knew them well because, a few years back, I was hired to help them organize the Colombian Squash Federation in our country.

The first time the squash players stayed with us, we received nine squash delegations that were to compete in the Pan-American Squash tournament held in Bogotá. This was a tournament played in several South American countries. Individual sports events have a participant competing individually during the event, and it is permissible that one country can register as many participants as the rules allow. For this event, squash delegations varied from one athlete from Paraguay, to twelve members in the Colombian delegation.

Our Inn was chosen to accommodate them for a week in Bogotá. Although we were proud to be the selected as the official lodging for Bogotá, we were a little concerned because, in Medellin squash players had been accommodated in a luxury hotel. Our concept was different because it was homelier and less expensive. Certainly, we could not compete with the lavish amenities they were accustomed to, but we could with our hospitality and service. We were prepared to make them feel at home, by exceeding their expectations. Our philosophy was successful. Days later, members of the Brazilian women's squash team told me how grateful they were, because during their stay at our Inn, they had bonded to become a real team.

In their particular case, when they were going to compete, as so many athletes came from different cities, the Brazilian team met for the first time at the airport. For that reason, large hotels were not their preferred choice. They preferred staying in small hotels so they were able to bond, and where they could get to know each other better. Therefore, the players from Brazil indicated that the atmosphere at the Inn was the most welcoming. The living room and the Inner courtyard became instant gathering places for all the sports delegations. All the players got together to discuss their daily results and future competition in a very pleasant environment. Considering that squash was a new sport in Latin America, it was interesting to see how, by the end of this tournament, these athletes not only gained experience competing, but in many cases became good friends.

A NUISANCE IN A SPORTS DELEGATION

Athletes tend to be more disciplined than normal guests; but, with one particular team, there was an exception: Jose, a character, who turned out to be a big nuisance.

He was part of a sports delegation from a Central American country. His features were clearly indigenous; and he was of medium height with an athlete's body. In the mornings after breakfast, all the participants were required to be in the event venue, the sports club. Some were going to train and others to compete; but with Jose, the story was different. Since his arrival, he was reluctant to go to training, and always had excuses for his coach. To make matters stranger, once his teammates left, he asked the front desk for the yellow pages and made several calls during the day. The next day, he would need the yellow pages again. This made me horribly suspicious: was he looking for drugs? Each call received by the front desk was more suspicious than the last one; the callers' voices seemed to come from shady characters with no education. In the past, we had, had several foreign guests who had arrived in Colombia looking for drugs; so we suspected something strange. For those who tried similar things and were discovered, without hesitation we asked them to leave. For all intents and purposes, Jose gave us the same impression; he was searching for a drug dealer.

Fortunately, on the third day Jose put our concerns to rest, when he announced that a cousin was coming to visit him. That Friday after lunch, as I was saying goodbye to the girls from the Brazilian delegation as they hurried off to practice; when an old clunky cab rolled up, creaking and groaning as it parked in front of our Inn. A very obese black woman with a light brown colored wig descended from the vehicle. She wore a close fitting tiger skin patterned t-shirt with a deep neckline, and fishnet nylons with high laced shoes that matched her t-shirt. What was most striking about her was her makeup: bright lime green color eyelids, shockingly red lips and long false eyelashes.

She needed no introduction, I recognized her instantly. I have seen these women in the news, and I knew her trade: *"My God,"* I thought; I was about to have a confrontation with a prostitute in the parking lot of our Inn.

I was not sure what to do. I prepared myself mentally. I was worried because I didn't want the neighbors to see her and believe we were turning our stylish neighborhood into a slum frequented by prostitutes and drug dealers.

Despite my prayers, the woman headed toward us. I stood blocking her entrance when she reached the door.

"Can I help you?" I asked politely.

"I am here to visit the guest in room 102" she replied confidently.

I answered without letting her in. "Wait one moment please, I'll see if he is around."

On my way to room 102, I was surprised to find Jose in the living room. I said to him: "There's a woman here to see you, Jose."

"She is my cousin. Can you can let her in?" he explained nervously.

"Absolutely not," I replied without hesitation, "and do me a favor; do not invite her again."

Speechless, he went to the door to meet her. I knew this woman had heard our conversation because the entrance to the living room was close to where she was standing at the front door. As we arrived at the Inn's front door, she was in a rage.

"Don't worry, there are many cheap hotels in this area", she spat, giving me an angry look. I stared back at her emotionless and did not give in.

Jose left hastily, but not before he closed the door so hard that my employees thought he had broken it. I took a deep breath and felt relieved. It had been my first serious incident and I overcame it without any sort of scandal. One of the biggest concerns for a young hotelier was dealing with these kinds of women as they can get very aggressive. I felt relieved as in my first encounter with a prostitute, I had protected the integrity of the Inn without causing too much of a scene.

After the shock, I went to the kitchen to talk to Doris, our restaurant Manager. I told her what had just happened. She was a pleasing person with a friendly nature. She is a member of the Mormon Church and abides by their doctrines to the letter. As I was telling the story she began to blush, and at one point in my telling the story I thought I was offending her, because Doris did not say a word. Suddenly, she dropped a bomb:

"I think it was my fault" she explained.

I did not understand her reaction,

"What are you talking about?"

She told me that Jose mentioned that he was extremely stressed out; so she advised him: "What you need is a massage".

But what Doris didn't know was that there are massages done by therapists, and there are those given by "masseuses", another name for prostitutes. We were laughing about this confusion when Jose came back. He looked dazed and apologized to us. Up until the time he left, Jose was never a problem again.

To our surprise, Jose's team was flying to Paraguay to play another tournament before returning to their country. On their flight back to their Central American country, their itinerary scheduled a one-night stay in Bogota, continuing their trip home the next day. At the request of the players, including Jose, they asked the coach if they could spend that night back the Inn. Therefore, the team returned one-month later; arrived very late at night and left very early in the morning. I was glad they had decided to stay with us.

CYCLING TRACK TEAM

Another delegation we had the fortune to accommodate for three weeks was the national cycling track team. Several cyclists stayed with us.

Cycling has blossomed into one of Colombia's most successful athletic programs. To date at least fifteen cyclists are winners at the international level.

Every morning they left to train on the hills north of the city. Watching them ride was quite a sight. They left the Inn early in the morning; riding to Sopo, a town 39 kilometers from Bogotá, and returned with incredible ease. Both the altitude and the steep hills around the city make for a tremendous training route. They did this ride in less than three hours.

Then they rested in their rooms for a while. After which they would continue their training by riding static bicycles in the corridors.

In the afternoons, they trained on the track.

Never during their stay did these cyclists present a problem. But, I was careful to advise the younger cyclists when they went to the drugstore to purchase flu medicines; I had to warn them to watch out for unauthorized substances in many of them. These young athletes believed us and, when they found it had an illegal substance, would discard it right away. Regular medicines can test positive for drugs testing done during a competition, and therefore, the cyclists must always be very careful. But this team definitely left us with the best memories of their hard work and discipline.

SQUASH TOURNAMENT

However, of all the groups of athletes that stayed with us, we befriended several squash players who came to participate in the squash championship each year; an event held at Club El Nogal. Since the inauguration of the Inn we had a great relationship with the club. The close distance between us and the club, allowed athletes to be able to walk between the

Inn and the club with ease. Every year, during the month of August, different squash players from different nationalities arrived to stay at the Inn. They came to participate in their prestigious tournament of this sport.

Before starting the Championship, in order to classify for the main draw many had to play the qualifiers. They had to compete for a few spaces left. Many of these players' travel at their own expense and did not qualify for free lodging at the club; so many of them returned to our Inn. Our rates and the close location to the Club was greatly appreciated by these athletes.

For this reason, February 7, 2003 left us in shock. The Club suffered one of the worst acts of terrorism that shook the city. 33 people were killed, with many others wounded and left disabled. It was 8:15 pm and I was at home when the attack occurred. I could not believe what had happened. Whenever news was available, television programs were interrupted for updates. The sight was terrible; only dead and injured people were shown throughout the night. Fortunately, our guests did not react to the noise; but it really struck all of us at the Inn at our core. A car bomb was parked in the parking space where it could do the most damage. However, the terrorists didn't know that the building had been constructed with the latest earthquake-resistant technology; which stopped them achieving their mission – to demolish the club.

From the start of the following day, we could not concentrate because for the several years we had worked with the Sports Department, we were sure that being a Friday evening, they all had to be working at the Club. Fridays was always the busiest day for them, as many members hire the club for events which could hold up to 500 people in different rooms. The whole thing was daunting. Fortunately, we learned by 10 o'clock in the morning, that all those we knew were safe and none had sustained injuries of any kind. On the other hand, it was terrible to know that the person who used to work as a squash instructor placed the bomb in his car and was counted as one of the dead.

Squash instructors were very scarce, and when the Club began the squash program, the Squash Federation recommended this person; who by no means appeared to be a member of a guerrilla group. Freddy had always behaved in a stylish manner, and he owned a nice car. At one point he purchased a membership of the club; something those who knew him were surprised by because no one knew he had the monies to do so. It became clear to the police during the investigation, that his membership had been financed by the terrorists. It was a way to have easy access to the club. Hence, they gave him the vehicle, and everything he needed to become a member. Furthermore, he established a company to pass himself off as a businessman.

What Freddy did not know was the fact that the terrorists were going to mislead him. He was instructed to park the car at 8:15 pm which would give him sufficient time to leave the club safely; the bomb was to be detonated at 10 pm. This did not happen. As soon as Freddy arrived and parked his car, a militant, who was closed by making sure the car was in the parking lot, used a remote device to explode the bomb. Obviously, he was not needed anymore.

All the stories of this tragedy hit us hard. Our receptionist Ricardo, was especially moved by a seventy-year-old man; who decided to rescue a child, who was alone and saved him.

It was remarkable considering that it was an act of courage that was to cost him his life. The effort made by this courageous man was such that his heart could not take the pressure, and he suffered a heart attack. The story moved us. Witnesses explained that he was in the process of coming out of the club when he heard a child crying, and without doubting it for one minute, he returned to help the child. Apparently this boy was under some debris, and this forced the 70-year old man to make an extreme effort, with terrible consequences. We were sad because we would have liked the ending to finish well; but life can be sometimes cruel.

The day was gray in every sense. All of us, including our guests, did not stop talking about this tragedy. Suddenly, a middle-aged man walked in to reception and demanded a room. It was 11 am and the Inn was completely full. We explained that check-out for our guests was at 12 pm., and until then, we did not have a room free. This man was completely disheartened and desperate, and after fifteen minutes of discussion with us trying to explain our situation;

He told me "you don't understand, my brother died last night trying to save a child and, I am here to make all the funeral arrangements".

We were amazed because it was precisely the story that had saddened us all. I suggested to him that, if he wanted to, he could leave his things with us so that he could go and make the necessary arrangements. He reacted well to my suggestion. We saw very little of him, but we know he managed to organize everything he had to do. We did not stop congratulating him on the courage of his brother, and I think that eased his sorrow a little.

After several months passed, the Club was rebuilt and they were able to re-start their programs. Unfortunately for us at the Inn, after new safety measures were implemented, the Squash competition was reduced to a minimum. Players were invited a week earlier for the qualifiers and they lodged them in the Club's hotel. The players could not leave the venue without specific permission, and at all times had to carry their identification. Visitors were allowed but the access was such an annoyance that many players decided not to return.

The sports department warned us about their new safety procedures, and after what happened to them, we understood the new measures. Due to this terrible experience, they were unable to schedule many open tournaments.

La Posada: short stories from an Inn

Misfortune and Troublemakers

La Posada: short stories from an Inn

These stories relate to men and while some encountered difficulties, others were basically troublemakers. I often felt exasperated by the antics of their actions, but in other instances I was extremely concerned. From the latter I include the following stories:

JOE

Joe, a thirty-year-old British man with brown hair and good looks, came to the Inn on a recommendation from the British Embassy. He was staying in an expensive hotel in the north of Bogotá and, had fallen in love with the area in which the Inn was located. However, his budget did not allow him to continue living in a lavish atmosphere, and he needed something less overpriced. After visiting the Inn and having a full guided tour, he decided to stay with us. He booked us for a very long stay according to his own words, and initially made an advance payment of two weeks. It gave us the confidence that he was going to be an excellent guest. Little did we know that the problems would arise sooner than later!

Joe made friends with a guest from New Zealand, who knew Bogotá very well. He was the best companion that Joe could have found because they both spoke English, and both had learned to move around the city with no problems. By the end of the month we were going annoying with the complaints about their continuous drunkenness. Furthermore, neither one obeyed the Inn's rules. The night receptionist fought with them every night because they always wanted to bring in call girls; something absolutely forbidden by the Inn and both knew this. Fortunately, the New Zealander decided to continue his journey around the world, and one day canceled his stay and left. When we required payment from Joe, he began to ask for more time. He explained to us that the money should arrive soon. We thought the Embassy was our backup and this would allow us to receive our payment on the room, but, our assumption was a terrible mistake.

Three months went by and he had not paid a cent. He seemed to be penniless but was successfully being continuously invited out by other guests. In exchange, as Joe knew the city very well, he volunteered to show them the tourist attractions. We believed that this is how he managed to survive. Until the day, I remember I decided to end his charade and ask him to pay his bill. It was a date I remember because it was my birthday. I went to his room to make sure he would not escape from this conversation. When I knocked on his door, he opened nervously and told me not to worry. He explained he was going to take a shower and leave to go the bank because was determined to pay what was owing. Towards noon he left, but he never returned. Joe was gone...

What was amazing is that he left all his clothes, documentation and suitcases. His whereabouts were a mystery because no-one had seen him. After three days, I decided to check with the Embassy and to make them aware of what had happened. The Embassy's employees were alarmed and told me that if they heard anything, they would keep me informed. We delivered his belongings, including the passport, to the Embassy. Regularly, they contacted us to find about if we had heard anything, and we would do the same. The days passed and nothing happened at all. Joe simply disappeared!

A month later, I received a call from the Embassy. They found him and worried about him. After many days of wondering about around the city, he ended up in an elegant brothel near Zona Rosa. There he went out of control, and without considering how quickly his bill was growing, invited several women to join him for champagne and parties. In four days, the invoice presented to him was of four million pesos. When they asked him to pay his account, he used the same ploy he had done with us and said to them,

"I'm going to the ATM and I will be back".

But this time, he went directly to the British Embassy to ask them for help. The situation was critical. Apparently, the owner of this establishment was into drug trafficking. The Embassy requested support from London, and a few days later Joe arrived to pay our account and apologize. We were sorry about what had happened to him. He was very scared, despite being under the care of his embassy. We heard through the grapevine that Joe had returned to London and hoped to continue touring the world again. Joe definitely did not learn his lesson.

GROUP OF 8

Joe left for good, and a few days later, we received a group of 8 people; who were accompanied by our good friend, the Mexican Consul. He looked distraught. He explained that the embassy had to pay this bill as this family was mugged when they entered Colombia through the Cucuta border post. From the first moment, while the Mexican Consul was telling their story, this group did not show any concern or emotion. Their attitude generated a huge level of distrust in all of us at the Inn. As the days passed, considering the details changed when they explained their story to other the guests, none of the employees believed in the assault.   According to the individual members of this family the assailants left them without money. This group would leave the Inn early after breakfast and would arrive back late in the evening; always happy, carefree, with shopping bags and fast food bags

We decided to undertake some research on our own. I asked my employees to ask different members of the family, the same questions. As the answers came in I found that the mugging incident at the border post was not true. There were many contradictions in every story they told considering they initially narrated that the mugging was done on a trail. We got different descriptions depending on who was narrating this horrifying incident. There was no mention at all of the bridge at the border post; the legal entrance over land into Colombia. Without hesitation I called the Consul. I told him about the daily activities of this group, and the different stories we had heard, and our views. After a few hours, he called me back.   He explained that they had communicated with other Mexican Embassies in South America; and, evidently, the Embassy in Brazil reported the same story. Apparently, this group's intention was to travel throughout South America for free, and they had no problem in using the same story everywhere. The Consul decided this group had to leave our Inn and find somewhere else to stay at their own cost.   The Mexican Consul thanked us for discovering this scheme, as it could have been expensive for the Mexican Embassy.   In addition, he warned other embassies not to fall into this trap, especially from this group.

SIGNOR PINO

Another disappointment was Signor Pino. He was a charming and very handsome man, of Italian descent with Canadian citizenship. He was so good looking he seemed more like a magazine model, than anything else. He lost his passport somewhere in Bogotá and the Canadian Embassy suggested that he stay at our Inn as he had to wait at least three days to get a new one.

The strange thing was that he never left the Inn and was on the phone all day. We didn't understand why he chose to stay with us, considering he looked like someone who could afford to stay in a more sophisticated place. At times, he would go to the street corner store to buy cigarettes; which would take him less than 30 minutes. He had no friends and no one came to visit him.

But one day, he went out as usual to the corner store and when he returned, he was accompanied by two men. They introduced themselves at the front desk:

"We are from Interpol and have come to arrest Mr. Pino. There is an Extradition Bulletin from three countries in Europe. He needs to return to pay his bill. We will be placing him in detention."

The surprise was huge, and left us speechless:

"What? There has to be a mistake. Our guest did not give us the impression he is a crook."

But the agents told us;

"Make no mistake, he takes advantage of his good looks".

Pino smiled nonchalantly, accepting these accusations. He proceeded to pay what he owed, leaving us bewildered.

A few weeks later, our telephone bill arrived. We had become another one on his victims' list. The statement showed an excess of one million three hundred thousand pesos, an exorbitant amount; there were at least 50 overseas calls. Pino had managed to change the security password code of our PBX telephone system; gaining access to international calls without our knowledge; each call lasting approximately 45 minutes. Not expecting this, we were challenged to pay the bill. We needed at least 5 people per night staying in our accommodation, and even then the payment was difficult. This confirmed that this thug was an electronics expert, and for this reason he was on the world most wanted lists.

THREE MEN

My following stories refer to three men that encountered terrible difficulties that they could have somehow prevented.

The first guest

This guest arrived with the support of his embassy. He registered as a Medical Doctor; was very attractive; tall, with a black beard and black hair. He looked to be in his late 30's but he was so thin it was difficult to predict his real age; it seemed to have suffered a bit. He was unhappy with our type of accommodation and didn't stop telling us that he had not chosen us; but he did not leave the Inn for any circumstances, and always looked miserable. One day, while he was sitting alone in the Inner courtyard, I decided to talk to him and see what we could do to improve his stay. Surprisingly, he opened up and told me his story. I was appalled how life can change in a minute. Particularly, in this case, the change was caused by drugs.

Guillermo was indeed a prestigious doctor with an impressive clientele. His life was surrounded by many luxuries. He explained; he drove a Porsche, owned a beautiful house with a swimming pool, and most importantly had a family he adored; but he managed to ruin everything. During a social event he felt tempted to try cocaine, and began using drugs daily. To make things worse, his access to the money he needed daily became limited and still he was unable to stop using drugs.

One day, he mentioned his concern to his supplier, who suggested a lucrative and audacious proposal. He suggested:

"It is very simple; go to Colombia and bring back your own stash. It will be cheaper."

He was excited about the idea because he could do drugs while spending less money. This idea became an obsession, to the point that Guillermo seriously began to think about traveling to Colombia. Because he trusted his supplier's connections, he asked the dealer for more information about how to make the purchase that would enable him to return home with the drugs he needed. The supplier assured him that everybody who went to Colombia looking for drugs returned without a problem; however, he would give him the necessary instructions which, to be successful, should be followed to the letter. This phrase (followed to the letter) was repeated several times so that he understood that if he didn't, he might end up in prison. Without thinking twice, Guillermo took a flight to Barranquilla where the necessary contacts were arranged. According to the instructions he had been given, he stayed at a luxury hotel. He did absolutely everything he was told to do. Days later, he received the drugs with the final instructions.

However, Guillermo was about to discover that, when people like him take their flight back home, he would be double-crossed by the drug traffickers. The drug traffickers get the word to authorities to search a particular passenger; who is undeniably loaded down with drugs. It enables the drug traffickers to get their own merchandise out of the country. Foreigners, in particular, are targets, and are used as bait on the different flights. A plane departing from Colombia can carry as many as five or more drug mules, therefore the drug lords must distract the authorities with their unsuspecting preys. When the doctor made the payment, the drug traffickers led him to believe that all would go well.

The next day, he left for the airport and passed through the first luggage control without a problem. Although he was extremely nervous, he tried to calm down to avoid being caught. Once the flight was called, he boarded the plane and sighed in relief, thinking the worst was over. However, to his surprise, he was called to the entrance of the aircraft, where, along with two other people, the flight supervisor asked him kindly to identify his luggage. Once he reached the tarmac, the police were waiting for him with dogs sniffing the suitcases. It did not take long to find the cocaine inside his luggage. Unaware about how the drug business really works, he was told, foreigners make popular targets and used as bait on the different flights.

If Guillermo had been an illiterate person with limited resources the judge may have shown some kind of mercy; but in this case the Judge was frustrated that Guillermo was a person with higher education, a Doctor, a brilliant professional career, and wealthy. The conviction was hard-hearted: a four-year sentence which should be done entirely in Colombia. Fortunately, there is the system which allows the reduction of sentences. Guillermo took part in all possible activities at the prison, including practicing medicine to the extent he was allowed.

When Guillermo arrived at the Inn, he was on his way home and was quite worried. Although his family would be happy to see him, the uncertainty of his future made him extremely anxious. His medical practice was non-existent and he didn't know if it was possible to recover it. We could not understand how someone so well qualified was duped in this way. This is a warning bell for those doing drugs and the terrible consequences it can bring.

Guillermo had to wait a few days until the authorities would give him the final permission he required to leave Colombia. The Immigration Department had to check with the Court to find out if he had effectively served his sentence, and only then would they give him their authorization so he could leave the country. Without this authorization the Immigration Officials at the airport would prevent his departure. The boredom and anguish were dreadful for him and as time passed, he became angrier, more arrogant and sarcastic with the employees at the Inn. Fortunately for the Inn employees, the embassy officials arrived; he could return him home.

La Posada: short stories from an Inn

The second guest

This next guest had a bizarre event that really shocked us all.

João was Brazilian, a colorful and suave character. My front desk employees made bets on this guest's real age, and we all failed in our attempts to guess. We were astounded; he was 75 years old, incredible! An athletic body without a single wrinkle, dark-skinned and his strange style of dress. He carried a bag from a store chain, and a leather case he possessively took care of; these were all his belongings. He registered as a semi-precious jewelry salesman and explained that the leather case was his showcase.

After working all day, João would arrive back at the Inn and go straight to his room; not leaving until the next day. We were not sure what he ate considering he never asked for breakfast to be included in his room rate. During the second day of his stay, Martha, one of my housekeepers, came into to my office smiling. She explained that João was somewhat "exposed" in the inner courtyard. He had been told that the inappropriateness of his dress was upsetting some guests. I quickly went to see what was going on and had to contain my laughter because he was only wearing a thong; he was trouser-less and shirtless. The picture was not pretty and it explained why the guests were uneasy. When I managed to talk to him, I asked him not to do it again. We didn't allow that mode of dress in our Inn. Although, he was not happy, he never appeared dressed like that again.

A few days later, the cleaning lady told me:

"I need you in room 101 because there is a smell that I am finding difficult to remove".

As soon as I entered the room I felt nauseated. The smell was extraordinarily strong. We tried to air the room but were unsuccessful. I declined to say anything to our guest anything because we expected to be able to solve this problem ourselves. But the longer João stayed, the worse the smell became. So, I decided to ask him what produced that strange odor in his room. He felt we had invaded in his privacy and politely informed me that it was not my problem. I had to answer and explain that categorically it was my problem, considering it affected a room at the Inn. He thought it for a few minutes and said:

"It comes from the herbs that keep me in shape. They come from the Amazon jungle, and that is why I am in such good health".

The next day, in what appeared to be his daily routine, João left the Inn to attend several appointments; but he never returned. Basically, he disappeared. We waited for two days and decided he had left without paying. His departure caused me annoyance because he had the advantage, as he was traveling with very little luggage. It is difficult to control a guest's departure when they are traveling light. Furthermore, João left nothing in the room to indicate that he would return. The worst thing was that linens and the mattress had to be professionally cleaned because were impregnated with that terrible odor.

Two years later, the João episode was forgotten and in the past, the front desk receptionist came to my office and told me:

"There is a Brazilian man who wants to pay a Bill."

I couldn't believe it. After two years, João had returned to pay his outstanding account, but what had happened to him surprised us all.

The day he left the Inn, he was heading to a small town four hours away from Bogotá. He had pre-booked appointments with various Jewelers and was excited because it looked as if he was going to have a good and productive day. His intention was to conduct his appointments and return to Bogota. João went by bus because it was the most practical way to travel. After two and a half hours of traveling, the bus was held up by the guerrillas. It was a difficult time for the country and all trips outside Bogotá had risks. Once, the rebels realized he was a foreigner, they took him off the bus and asked him to follow them. Fortunately, after twenty hazardous days on the mountain, the rebels found out he was simply a sales person and let him go; with terrible consequences. He was left at the side of the road and was able to return to the capital. João asked his embassy for help, which he received and he returned to Brazil. However, this trauma caused him a serious heart condition and he was not allowed to work for almost a year.

The moment he started to get his life back, he decided to quit his job abroad and work nearer to home. He had things that were unfinished and when you think about the trauma that he suffered, we were amazed by the honesty of this man; through all of his experiences he remembered the debt with us. We did not hear from him again but will be eternally grateful that he remembered us after such an experience.

The third guest

The following character was a single guest whose story endeared him to us.

Since we started to work at the Inn, at times, we had an unusual guest. This guest did not request a room but rather preferred to sleep late overnight in the Inn's front doorway.

German was a homeless man who arrived quietly in the early morning hours to sleep in the corner of the floor at our entrance. Despite our fruitless attempts to stop him, we managed to reach an agreement. Our agreement was that if he slept in the doorway, at the very least he did not use the entrance as a toilet.

For those who did not know him they feared him because of his scruffiness, but he was quite friendly. What was more confusing, was that he could engage in a very polite conversation for a few minutes; after which, he would rant about Star Wars and the alien enemies that caused him to panic and made him run away. This frequently occurred when he had a piece of aluminum foil on his head in the form of a helmet. This helmet served to defend him from these imaginary beings; the alien enemies.

His story intrigued me because, despite his rags, you could tell there was something that distinguished him from many other homeless people. He was different and always stayed close to our Inn. Whenever we spoke to him, he seemed to need our help because he did not like his life; but, at the same time, his madness did not help.

When we started with the restaurant we gained a lunchtime clientele. German waited patiently outside and I noticed that some of our clientele, as they left, gave him food. Some of our clientele talked to him as if they knew him well. I decided the next day to look for this group of clientele and ask them about German. Their response was terribly painful and it took me a while to recover. They told me that he had been a successful bank executive, who at the age of 28 had been promoted to Vice President with opportunities to progress his career abroad. His co-workers believed that due to the stress which resulted from his new position, he made the worst decision of his brilliant career, and took a narcotic drug that had literally driven him mad. He began to rave and continued to do so, until his family had to admit him to a clinic for the mentally ill. He had escaped from this clinic several times, and always arrived at a place near his home. Apparently his family lived in the same neighborhood, and he tried to be close to them.

For only reasons his crazed mind understood, he preferred to sleep outside, on the floor of our door, rather than sleep in the comfort of his own home. German only allowed his family to pick him up from time to time; when they would bathe him, cut his hair and shave him. His family would dress him in three clean sweaters, so he would not be so cold and being dressed in them it would be difficult for the sweaters to get stolen. Once this was done, they left him to venture out in the strange universe only he understood. Although they made attempts there was no way in which they could hold him at home, as all he wanted was to be on the street.

Ironically, he did not care about money. The first few times we saw him, we gave him coins, but he would look at them for a few minutes and then leave them in the frame of the reception desk window. For this reason, whenever we could, we offered him something to eat; which he always accepted, muttering his thanks. We saw him occasionally, and never knew where he was going, or why he came back again.

It was difficult for us to make our guests understand that German was harmless, friendly and they should have nothing to fear. Fortunately, he appeared very rarely during the day. One evening we heard terrible screams and ran out into the street to see what was happening. We saw two ladies who were guests, running towards us, screaming that someone had robbed them one block from the Inn. Behind them German was running towards them with two bags. These ladies, crying hysterically, pointed to him as the thief. When we calmed them down, we found out that they were walking towards the Inn without a care in the world, when at that moment German appeared from nowhere and because of his appearance, they got scared that decided to drop the bags and run towards the Inn. German picked up the bags and ran behind them so that he could give them the bags they had left behind. Once everyone was calmed down, bags were returned; we smiled at German so he knew that he had done nothing wrong. He was like a child who needed to know everything was alright.

The last time I had the opportunity to have a long talk with him was the day when a group of British guests arrived to check-in. I was at the entrance of the Inn talking in English to the group's guide, when I saw German standing behind me translating our conversation. I couldn't believe it, he understood English perfectly. When I finished talking with the group's guide, I turned around to see him, and for the first time since I had known him, he was not looking at me with strange eyes, but with the eyes of German, the successful banker. He seemed to clearly know what he was going to say:

"I speak English perfectly. I graduated from a bilingual school and studied International Finance Management".

Unfortunately, in less than ten minutes, he returned to his own unreal world. When that happened to him, he would leave quickly. Sadly, I didn't have another conversation with him, other than a few words to greet him with a wink or a smile.

Even though we knew German slept in our doorway, arriving late at night and leaving very early in the morning, we didn't see him for several months. The first thing in the morning at the Inn, we had to quickly clean the place because of his unbearable smell. At his last appearance one day I saw that he was limping badly. I was worried because one of his legs was considerably thicker than the other, looked swollen with a terrible color. I asked him what had happened and told us that when he tried to stay in a bakery doorway, someone shot him with a pellet gun to make sure that he would not stay there or return. German told us that it hurt him a lot. I tried to make him understand that the leg was in very bad shape and he should go to and see a doctor, but he looked at me as if he did not understand what I was saying. Nothing would make him get into a car, so we didn't try and take him to the hospital. We got him something to clean the wound and gave him the items in a bag. We were sure nothing was going to happen as German did not understand what he had to do. He needed someone to treat his leg but we did not know who could help him. Everyone at the Inn knew that his family lived nearby and although we did not know the address, we hoped that one of his family or friends saw him before the wound got worse.

After a few days, the news reached through one of the

merchants in our area; German never woke up from sleeping in one of his favorite places. I think he deserved to be at peace. He could not continue fighting his demons, who did him much harm in a world that was certainly not for him.

Despite our intentions, without being able to do much, we strived to help German. I always felt he wanted his crazy mind to allow him to engage in a conversation with me; but, he would give up easily and when he couldn't do it, just walked away.

Unfortunately for German, life didn't spare him from his big mistake.

La Posada: short stories from an Inn

Women

La Posada: short stories from an Inn

I was touched and frustrated on occasions with some of the women staying with us. Several because of difficult circumstances, loneliness, drug trafficking, and child exploitation; while others enjoyed a beautiful change of their lives, these are their stories.

MARIA ELVIRA

It was a Monday morning and I was unprepared, but looking forward to a great week at the Inn. Therefore, I was quite curious when I saw Maria Elvira coming down the stairs; she was a lady who was approaching sixty years old, with distinguished flair, and as my grandmothers used to say "someone who must have been very pretty in her youth." She looked like the owner of the house, felt very much at home to the point that she was wearing her nightgown in the hallway of the Inn. As I greeted her, I noticed that she had a black eye and a bandaged arm. I tried to understand this woman; she never stopped talking, and followed me everywhere; was always friendly and polite, but made me anxious because she talked non-stop and I had only been at the Inn for an hour.

Deciding to be patient with her, as soon as I could, I asked her not walk around the Inn in her nightgown because this would definitely upset our other guests. She honored my request during her stay and I did not have to worry anymore.

In one of her endless long talks, she decided to tell me her story; and although I knew I was going to have to pay attention for a long time; it was true that she needed someone to listen.

She graduated from one of the most prestigious bilingual schools of Bogotá, and could certainly be appreciated by her demeanor, and fluency in English. During a social event in Bogotá, she had met a UN official to whom she had been married to for more than twenty years. They had a son who lived in Chicago, United States, and she spoke to him frequently. From all the years she was married; because of her husband's job on UN missions around the world, her most vivid memories was her stay in Mozambique, Africa. She described the beautiful mansion they had lived in, with several employees at their service. It was close to the sea which allowed them to watch the most beautiful sunsets. Because of her husband's position, they had splendid parties several days a month which were attended by diplomats and personnel from various international organizations. They also received many invitations from their friends, and all this entertaining made her stay in this country incredibly pleasant. She gave us an unbelievable picture of Africa; its beaches, its amazing sunsets, and the reasons why she fell in love with it. She had been very happy.

But, all of this came to a terrible end. Maria Elvira explained that her marriage ended abruptly because her husband left her for another woman. She was blindsided, considering that for twenty years she had been a stay-at-home mom and never realized things were outside her control. In their settlement, her husband suggested she should return to Colombia, where he bought her an apartment so that she could live rent free.

We spent several days trying to understand why she had ended up at the Inn. Where was her family? Following her many stories, we were able to conclude that her brothers lived in the United States, and her mom, the only one who lived in this city, suffered from a very advanced stage of Alzheimer's. Her brothers paid a woman to take care of their mom.

When Maria Elvira returned to the country, she wanted to live with her mother, but she was unable to get along with her mom's caretaker. One night this woman assaulted Maria Elvira physically, leaving her with a black eye and a twisted arm; the reason why she ended up living at the Inn.

Fortunately for Maria Elvira, her gentle and loving character allowed her to easily adapt to her new circumstances. Additionally, for us she was the ideal guest, she paid her account promptly, was clean and organized. Her only problem was her eagerness to make friends, and her endless conversations drove everyone crazy. Whoever sat next to her ended up dumbfounded, and the moment they could leave they left her alone. Pretty soon, Maria Elvira adjusted to her new budget, and was able to spend money on small pleasures. Happily, she decided to take some art classes, which occupied her during several mornings of the week. Occasionally she visited friends, and was slowly learning to be less passionate in conversations with the other guests; she began to notice that no one wanted to be by her side for long.

Maria Elvira talked about her boyfriend, an Austrian medical doctor who loved her. She told us that she might go to live with him. However, from the moment she arrived she never got a letter or a call from him. We didn't know if it was a fantasy, but we thought that if it made her happy we wouldn't spoil her dreams. She continually planned her trip to Europe and kept going to a travel agency.

Surprisingly one day, she announced that she was leaving to

go to Cartagena for a couple of months. We were all happy for her because we felt that a change of scene would do her good. Her mother was now so ill that she did not recognize her. Unfortunately, that weekend her mother died and Maria Elvira called me on Sunday afternoon to tell me that the funeral was at 10 in the morning, the next day. That Monday was a holiday and as I had a family commitment I was unable to attend, but sent her my deepest sympathies.

When I arrived at the Inn the following day, I found out that Maria Elvira had checked out. Initially, I thought that maybe she had decided to go to the coast, but at the end of the afternoon, I got a call from a well-known hostel located downtown Bogotá. German, the owner of the establishment and a good friend of our Inn, wanted to know what was wrong with Maria Elvira. She had checked in early that day and had everybody at the hotel exasperated. I asked him to be patient and understand that someone, who in the last year alone had an unpredicted cruel life change. Without giving him many details, I also told German about the funeral of her mother the day before. He appreciated the information and accepted her without concern.

Two weeks passed and suddenly German called me again. Was I ready to hear another peculiar story about Maria Elvira? He just wanted to let me know that he was quite worried because she had gone for a walk the day before and had never returned. German called me several times after that to find out if we had news of her, but no, I had no news. We had received several calls asking for her; especially from the seamstress who explained that Maria Elvira had asked her to make some clothes and paid up front for them. She never heard from her again and did not know what to do. All of this was very strange, because the person we knew was reliable with everything; appointments, commitments, and payments. I recommended German keep her things for a while and if I heard anything, I would let him know immediately.

A few days later, during a formal dinner I was approached by a cousin I saw occasionally. Juanita began to tell me about Maria Elvira and how she had been very happy at the Inn. She added; "You took good care of her." I was surprised because I was not aware they knew each other. It is then when I found out that they were school classmates and good friends. When Maria Elvira was attacked by the caretaker looking after her mother, it was Juanita who gave her the information about our Inn. Maria Elvira had decided it was a good option, and stayed with us for six months.

The strange thing is that at one point I grasped my cousin was talking in the past tense when referring to Maria Elvira; so I asked her:

"Do you know her whereabouts?"

And her answer astounded me:

"Didn't you know? She died".

It was a shock because during the months at the Inn she had never showed signs of being sick; however, she would repeatedly say that she did not want to die alone. I was upset because that is exactly what happened to her; she died alone in an emergency room of a renowned clinic of the city. Apparently the day she went for a walk in the center of the city, she felt sick and was able to get to the clinic, where a few hours later she died.

I asked Juanita for relatives and she told me that they came for the funeral but had returned to the United States. The next day, I called German to let him know the details I had received the day before. Needless to say he was as surprised as I was. It shocked and saddened us both; Maria Elvira's loneliness. No one called to ask or showed interest in her personal things, and considering no-one cared they ended up in two garbage bags. Apparently, many knew of our existence and that her final stop was at German's hotel. Yet, no one called to inquire about her belongings, and since there was no interest, we decided the best thing was to donate her belongings to a charity. It seemed to be the most appropriate thing to do. This story had a great impact on all of us and, most especially on me because I am blessed with a family I can always count on. It took several days for everybody at the Inn, and German, my hostel colleague, to stop thinking about this sad story.

OLIVIA

Soon after, unusual for the Inn, we had a walk-in guest. Standing in front of reception was a young woman, who was a bit strange in her ways. When I saw her, I was watchful for any eventuality and decided to attend her personally. My intuition was so strong that I advised our front desk to be prepared.

Olivia arrived with a bag full of clothes. She was young, no more than twenty-five years old, physically very skinny, extremely pale and with a strange look. Her appearance was terrible because her thinness made her look extremely sick. In addition, as she would never look me in the eye, she generated a distrust. Someone recommended the Inn to her and she wanted to stay with us for a couple of weeks. I asked Ricardo, from the front desk, to check room 206, and I informed her that it was the only one available. We used this room to discourage "possible unwanted" guests, because it was easy to dismantle it. Hence, we told her that we didn't think it would be to her liking because the room was in a state of disrepair. However, she quickly replied:

"I want to see it anyway."

When I opened the door, Olivia immediately said:

"It's perfect. I want to stay here for several days and I will pay in advance".

Following my intuition, I suggested that she pay for only five days, as our accounting program did not allow a longer advanced payment period. We were unable to discourage her, and nothing we said seemed to stop her from wanting to stay at the Inn.

Our problems with her began the following day. Considering that she had not left her room all day, housekeeping knocked on her door. She opened the door but blocked the entrance. Olivia informed our housekeeper that she was not interested in getting her room cleaned. Blanca, our employee, quickly came down to my office to let me know what the guest had just said. The worst part was that the room already smelled terrible. Furthermore, Olivia had blankets blocking the windows and giving the room a gloomy darkness. Evidently, she did not leave the room, and at night, noises were heard coming from her room.

The night receptionist had to knock at her door several times to ask her to stop making those noises because they were upsetting several other guests. As the Inn was an old house, she was asked to consider others.

The next day, we heard a thunderous noise coming from Olivia's room, and we ran upstairs to see what was happening. Despite knocking several times, she did not respond. I told her that I would not go away until she opened the door because she owed me an explanation about the noise coming from her room. When she finally opened the door, the room smelled terrible because of the poor ventilation. The racket we had heard, had been caused by the weight of the blankets, which had knocked down the blinds. Despite this, she continued with the blankets at the windows which were hanging onto the window hooks; giving the room the look of a rundown hospice. I sent Ricardo, one of the employees, to fix the blinds, but she insisted on keeping him out. I had to personally attend to the situation. When I confronted her, she notified me that:

"My religion does not allow me to speak or see men."

I tried not to laugh and to keep calm. However, I forcefully told her:

"Miss, you cannot remain in this room with broken things, so please let this employee in to do the necessary maintenance immediately".

In line with her strange attitude, she closed the door. Seeing that I was not going away, she informed me from the inside of the room:

"I will be out in 15 minutes."

After a short time, she left. Throughout the incident, we became aware that evidently, she only communicated with women. Taking into consideration that we did not know how long she was going out for, in a short time we cleaned and fixed the damage to the room.

After a few hours she returned and did not speak to anyone. She stayed for three more days but never left the room. On the fifth day, she came down with her things and said: "I'm leaving," mumbled something no one understood and left.

I could not believe what had happened, and could not understand her because she apparently did not have a soul in her life that cared for her. Five days at the Inn, and she did not receive a call or a visit from anybody. What was clear to us is that she lived in a very strange world. It seemed Olivia was alone, and there was no interest in her, just a terrifying loneliness.

Powerlessness

My two stories that follow, gave me huge concern about their safety, as they were in danger from the moment they registered at the Inn.

CONNIE

From the moment Connie came to the Inn, surrounded by four foreign black men who spoke to her in a derogatory manner, we assumed she was at imminent risk.

La Posada: short stories from an Inn

She was a Danish citizen, and although only 28 years old, seemed much older; with light blonde hair, obese and vulgar in her appearance. What shocked us most was her face, it was full of wrinkles like someone who had suffered very much or was into drugs. Connie heard about us from the airport information desk.

From the start, we understood that her relationship with these men seemed strange; they were fully controlling, most especially when they had something to say to her. Fortunately, these characters did not stay with us, they only came to pick her up every day. However, when she was told they had arrived, she panicked. The strangest thing was that she was coming from Nigeria, as were these men.

Days later during a conversation, she explained that she had been living in said African country for several years, which is where they met. We became suspicious of the reasons she ended up in Nigeria, and this gave us a warning signal for the whole situation. Besides which, Connie did not know why the men had traveled to Colombia. The indication was that it had to do with drug trafficking. Furthermore, we considered that the intention of these men was to send her back as a drugs mule; something we wanted to avoid at all costs. The Immigration Department report had been already filled out when she arrived, but we wanted to alert the Unit about this passenger. She had the specific characteristics of being a potential mule, and worst of all was under threat. Those who become mules generally are people who have serious financial problems, or do so, as in this case, by being threatened by a drug trafficker. All of us at the Inn wanted to find a way to protect her.

The detective chosen to help us, arrived at the Inn and

registered as a guest. With his experience, we were hopeful could identify such strange characters. On the second day of Connie's ordeal, after spending all day the Nigerians, she came back crying. She asked me if I knew where her country's Consulate was. Taking advantage, as these men were not around, I spoke to her because we wanted her to avoid any trouble with the police. Unfortunately, she only looked at me with fearful eyes but did not say a word. I gave her the Consulate's phone number, and she spoke to Madam Consul in their own language. Once she hung up, Connie told us that the Consulate advised her to stay at another place. A few days later, we received a call from the Consulate telling us that Connie was OK, and not to worry. This did not last long because the next day, I received a call from Connie, she was crying. Her Nigerian friends had taken her to a rundown hotel in the Center of the city, and she only wanted to return to our Inn. I knew she did not speak a word of Spanish, but asked if she could describe the numbers or signs she saw out the window. With this information, I reported to the Immigration Department the latest developments. Detectives went to the place she described, but did not find her. However, to our surprise that same afternoon Connie returned to our Inn. We asked her how she found us, to which she replied:

"The consul gave me the address again."

I decided to talk to Madam Consul and ask her; who was this person staying with us. I found out that she had the same concern. When she advised Connie to move to another Inn it was because the other Inn was administered by a Danish citizen. Madam Consul believed she might feel less vulnerable and peaceful at an Inn administered by someone Danish; but it didn't work. The moment Connie registered, she decided to discuss things with other guests that shocked them. Considering that this Inn is used by couples who have arrived to adopt a child, and need to finalize the adoption process; the owner was not interested in having someone so troublesome staying. Hence, she was politely asked to leave, and of course, she came back to our Inn. We told Connie that she was welcome this time, but under no circumstances could accept the men who came with her. Strangely, they did not show up, but at the end of the fourth day, she came back but then left very quickly, and we never saw her again.

I called the Immigration Department again, to inquire about her, because I felt overwhelmed at not being able to help her more. They informed me, she was staying at an infamous hostel located downtown Bogotá. As we expected, a couple of months later she was caught and sent to prison for a lesser charge. Fortunately, her prison time was no more than three months, and I was glad this happened because she got rid of the men. Furthermore, I was told that the Immigration Department gave a good report to the Court trying her case and the detectives involved in her situation where sure she was at risk from the moment she arrived to Colombia. Anything she did was done under distress therefore, they should consider those circumstances.

Connie gave us the impression that she had a huge debt with these Nigerians, because on her own she was unable to leave them. She had to pay them but this didn't work because as always only drugs lords win. Despite our good intentions, we were unable to do much, to stop her becoming a drugs mule. Once out of prison, she flew back home and hopefully will remember this terrible ordeal. Serious suffering can be avoided if only young people believed those with a little more experience.

SIXTEEN?

My next story was another case of powerlessness, when we could not do anything for someone at risk. In this case had to do with child prostitution.

The Inn received a guideline from the National Tourism Directorate, requesting us not to allow minors to register with adults who were not their legal parents, to prevent child prostitution at all costs. Until then we did not have a single case because we were careful in respect to children registering. For this reason, I was surprised when I arrived that day and saw a couple leaving from the front desk and heading towards their assigned room.

I immediately felt alarmed because the girl definitely looked very young. I asked our front desk receptionist, Ricardo, what kind of relationship they had; father and daughter? Ricardo was speechless because he had forgotten to ask for her ID. It was not enough for me, and I had to take action in this matter; to make sure nothing would happen to that child. I thought I would them the benefit of the doubt, and was going to wait until this couple left for any reason, and I could ask for the girl's identity card.

But one hour after they arrived, Martha, the housekeeper on the first floor, came running into my office. She was worried because she could hear, what appeared to be the man hitting the girl in the room. We went to the indoor courtyard, and it was clear that the man was beating his companion. It seemed to be never-ending.

I asked one of the male employees to knock on the door and ask if everything was OK. Nobody answered, but at least the noise ended; but we were bewildered. Very shortly afterwards the couple left and then returned rather quickly. The girl came in hiding behind the man she was traveling with. Ricardo was repairing a bench in the indoor patio and saw them pass by; he told us that the girl had a black eye. Fortunately, the male guest left after a short while. I went running to their room and knocked several times, but no one opened the door. Nevertheless, I was determined and told her if she didn't open the door I would bring in the police. Shyly she finally opened the door and walked out the room; I asked her:

"With whom are you traveling?"

She answered without flinching:

"My uncle."

Then I asked:

"How old are you? I want to see your citizenship card."

To which she answered that she didn't travel with it. I asked her age one more time, and when she saw I wasn't going to give up, she confessed to being sixteen years old. My next question was to ask if her parents knew about her trip, but she did not answer; she just remained speechless. I returned to my office quickly to call the National Tourism Directorate, and ask for guidelines about this situation. At that precise moment, the girl showed up at the front desk with their two suitcases. She paid for the night although they only stayed 4 hours at the Inn, and left in the car that came to pick her up. Who knows where she went and what could happen to this girl, as she apparently had no one to protect her. Unfortunately, the timing didn't give us the opportunity to notify authorities. We had no evidence and they never returned. This incident with this young girl could not be repeated at the Inn; and while we could, we ensured it did not happen again.

The reason for this problem starts with the dreams of minors, who, because of limited income earning opportunities in our country, dream to find a way to live an extravagant life. Unfortunately, their reference is the idyllic lifestyle shown on a television series; one which is related to drug trafficking. The plot in these programs are always the same; adolescents and young women of limited financial resources between 16 and 22 years of age, are sought by drug lords for their own pleasure; at a very high cost and risk to themselves. These television programs' ratings are very high because they show minors what they want to become. However, and, despite the fact that many of these girls are abused and have been killed, their purpose is to find men who can give them their desired lavish lifestyle in exchange for sexual favors. The most amazing thing of all of this is. that in many cases, the parents of minors and young women are indulgent because they also receive financial benefits, and their daughters become their financial sustainability. For this reason, the Government protects these young women by force; and here it is absolutely forbidden for a minor to register at a hotel with a man who is not her parent.

ADRIANA

Another guest that caused me many frustrations was Adriana, who arrived one day from Venezuela. She was young, attractive and had something special because men were instantly attracted to her. Her character was very odd because she was always on the defensive, and with women she was quite distant and aggressive. Because she was proud of working for her country's Revolutionary Government because she worked for it, she didn't allow any comment about it. She came to do a job at the national library, and every day she went out to work on her research and then returned in the afternoon.

During the first day she met Alejandro, a young Argentinian with a Colombian mother; she and Alejandro were exactly the same age. He was staying for just one night but, at first site, she mesmerized him. Without pondering the consequences, he postponed his trip to be able to stay with Adriana for as long as possible. After the second day they requested only one room for both of them, and looked as if they had known each other all their lives.

But things started to get complicated, because Joe, one of our frequent guests, arrived. He was a crew member with a U.S. airline, quite adorable, and the Inn's number one fan. Joe was of medium height, twenty-five years old with blond hair, and although he was not handsome, had an extremely gentle and loving nature. Because he loved coming to Bogota, depending upon his days off, we expected him every two or three months. Added to which, through the years he had been our best promoter. Thanks to his comments and references, we received many passengers.

When he met Alejandro and Adriana that same day, they formed a great friendship. To our surprise, two days later Adriana left very early from Joe's room and went to work. After a while, Alejandro came to the front desk asking if we had seen her; the receptionist said to him:

"I believe she left", and surprisingly enough, he did not ask any more questions.

Finally, to make matters more complicated, Osham, a Brit of Turkish descent, arrived from the airport. He was also a young man, twenty-five years old, physically very handsome because his penetrating green eyes contrasted with his tanned skin. During breakfast Osham became good friends with Alejandro and Joe. Because Joe, the American, had visited the city on several occasions, they decided that he would be their guide. They walked all day, visiting La Candelaria and other historical monuments, and when they arrived back in the afternoon they waited for Adriana to return from work. All of them went out to have fun. They enjoyed a very long night and all of them returned very much intoxicated. We believe that was what caused us the second surprise of the week, as Adriana spent the night in Osham's room. We couldn't believe it because she was Alejandro's girlfriend, and yet she flirted with the other two. After a few days, they all left for to travel to a different city: Adriana to Caracas, Alejandro to Cali, Joe returned to Miami and Osham flew to the Atlantic coast.

A month later, because he enjoyed our city, Joe returned again. He surprised us because he told us that he had decided to move to Caracas since he was very much in love and was currently living with Adriana. For him moving was very easy; because, for his work, he could do the required flights per month, and for his break days return to Caracas. Joe showed us pictures of both of them, giving us clear proof that they were a couple. More surprises as Joe and Adriana arrived, as a couple, one month later. Again she came to work and he, simply came to accompany her. Their stay lasted a week, and they left early on the Tuesday.

95

The next day, Alejandro showed up arriving from Cali. He explained that he was meeting Adriana. She had told him that she was going to be in Bogotá for a few days, working. He was enthusiastic about this meeting, because he thought he was very much in love. He was seriously thinking about proposing marriage. I tried to inquire how much he knew about this woman. He explained that they conversed a lot, but we knew from her part there were only lies. Until that point, his dramatic romanticism and love for this undeserving person made it unbearable for me. Hence, I stopped being discrete and asked him:

"Do you know where Adriana was last week?"

Alejandro responded, "Sure, she was traveling throughout Central America on a mission."

That was it! I then proceeded to show him the guest book pointing out Adriana's signature from eight days before. I also told him:

"Please read the name that follows."

When he realized that she and Joe had recently been at the Inn together, he was flabbergasted. This woman had been deceiving him for months, and had not been able to tell him the truth. Although I knew it was going to be a terrible blow, he needed to know the real Adriana. It was best if he started to look for another girl, one that could give him true happiness. Without uttering a word, he immediately broke her picture into a thousand pieces and threw it into the waste-paper basket of the living room. The next day, he departed to Buenos Aires. Fortunately, Adriana did not return again. We couldn't believe the suffering she caused through her terrible selfishness.

GLORIA

Fortunately, in other instances, we were able to contribute and help someone achieve someone happiness, as described in my following story.

One Friday afternoon, I saw Gloria, one of our guests, coming and going through the hall waiting for calls. She looked worried, so I dared to approach her and asked:

"Are you okay?"

She replied:

"I am marrying the love of my life tomorrow morning at the San Diego Church, and the only thing I have is the wedding dress and the Church. I need flowers, a small reception venue and a vehicle to take me to the Church."

She worked in Pasto, a city located south, near the border with Ecuador. Her boyfriend was employed by a government entity with its headquarters in Bogotá. Neither one could leave their job, because they both needed them; but at the same time, their ten-year relationship required a more serious commitment. While they were very much in love, they took a bold decision and decided to marry. They would remain in their different jobs seeking ways to frequently see each other. Living apart and so far apart could be a problem; yet they decided to give it a try. It was a question of managing time and distance, and they had planned it well.

Given this wonderful story, I had to step in and help her as much as possible. I had an appointment at 5 pm but still had two hours to help her in every way I could. The flowers for the Church and the bridal bouquet were easy to arrange, since there was a florist just in front of San Diego's Church. The owner committed to help us, and they would arrange the flowers at the altar early in the morning. Her bouquet would be ready for her at the door. The reception was our next concern, and although our restaurant did not work on Saturdays, we reached an agreement with Doris, the administrator, who promised a reception menu which included a wedding cake. Finally, we needed a car, and car rentals were too expensive for this couple's budget. An idea came to my mind; I dared to ask Gloria if she would mind going in my car, a Volkswagen Beetle, at no cost. She agreed gratefully, but now I needed a driver. When Hector, the night receptionist, came in and learnt about the arrangements, he volunteered to be the driver and take the bride to Church. After finishing all the arrangement for the wedding, I went home satisfied and pleased.

The next day, I arrived early to see her leave for the Church. We tied a huge white bow to the aerial of my car. Hector was wearing his best suit and tie, and looked very elegant for the occasion. What struck me the most, is that he was feeling very proud of his part in helping this couple, and obviously, he didn't charge them anything either. When they arrived at the Church the bouquet was waiting for them, and Hector went to park the car where classy limousines bringing brides to the Church, park. My Beetle didn't fair badly at all, on the contrary, it heightened the curiosity of the tourists passing by the place. Many photographs were taken of my car, and one was given to Hector, who came to show me the photograph with great pride. The wedding party was sensational, and seeing Gloria happy was good enough for us. Later in the afternoon when the guests had left; they left to go on a very short honeymoon, to visit the countryside of Boyacá.

MARLENE

Another interesting case was when I met Marlene. She came from the airport with her husband, and from the moment she registered, I was impressed by her tremendous outgoing and friendly personality. She proved to be a charming and self-confident woman. Because they were coming to visit her family, they stayed with us for three weeks. Her appearance was something else, she basically didn't care what she wore, and therefore she looked always extremely informal. Moreover, she wore her hair in a messy curly style, and her face, with its Latino features, was without any makeup. The fun part was that she did not seem to care about comments directed at or about her; but talking to her for ten minutes was a lesson of being positive, of moving forward and that nothing was impossible. She has been married to Tom for 15 years, a Canadian petroleum engineer, who was tall, handsome, and noticeably very much in love with his wife.

The next day, before they left to visit her family, she came into my office. I dared to ask her how they met:

"You are lucky, where did you meet him?"

But she quickly corrected me:

"He was the fortunate one."

What a response; in our culture it is always assumed that the woman is always the lucky one, and for that reason, she told me her story. About 15 years ago, Tom was in Bogotá doing business with the Colombian oil company. One day, by chance he took the same bus Marlene was on as she was coming home from school. He was immediately captivated by her and took a chance. When she got off the bus, he did the same. He thought it was his fate. As she started to walk home she was not worried, but suddenly she realized he was following her; then started to get nervous. As she arrived home, she rang the doorbell hoping someone would open the door quickly. Once the door opened, she rushed through and closed it quickly behind her, leaving this stranger standing on the street. Not wasting any time, after few minutes had passed, he rang the doorbell. Marlene had already warned her mother about what had happened on the bus, and how this character followed her to their house. They decided to open the door. Tom came in nervously. He introduced himself to Marlene's mother and explained that his intentions were honorable; he only wanted to woo and marry her daughter. Everything seemed absurd, but she accepted what he said because Marlene was attracted by the boldness of this daring Prince. She thought giving him the opportunity to pursue her was worth a try, and fifteen years later she had not regretted it for a moment because those memories remained very special to her.

They visited Marlene's family for two weeks and we were sad to see her go, but they had to go back to Canada which was their place of residence. We hoped they would return soon because they were a couple who definitely left an indelible mark on all of us. Two weeks later, we received a card through the mail; her thank-you note.

BERTA

Marlene's story reminded us of something similar that happened to a manicurist from the hairdressing salon located near us. Berta was petite, not graceful, unconcerned about her appearance, but a lovable and funny character. She met an English man during a family outing, who became absolutely fascinated with her. When he returned to his country, he wrote her very long letters that Berta had to ask for help translating because she did not understand the language. She enrolled in English classes so that she could try to understand him when they spoke over the phone. Fortunately, their communication was usually done in letters, which made life easier for both of them.

After a few months he asked her to marry him, inviting her immediate family to London where they could get married. She objected strongly and told him that if they could not get married in Colombia, she would not do it at all. Berta was so determined that the groom decided to organize the wedding in our country. He even brought her the wedding dress. They had a good time; they showed him how we dance and ate a typical Colombian meal. After the ceremony they left for London. Two years later, she returned to visit her family and friends. One of our employees was related to Berta's family, and after having lunch with her, began to tell us the whole story.

She showed us different pictures of Berta's home with her husband. The house was a mansion on the outskirts of London with its own stable of horses. Her father-in-law turned out to be a noble lord with a title that her husband would surely inherit. She seemed to have adjusted because she looked content with a spouse that obviously adored her.

It was like a story taken from a fairy tale. Everything that surrounded their romance is an example that life can give good people a quite unexpected change of fortune.

Internet Romances

La Posada: short stories from an Inn

Couples meeting on the internet has become a trend, and in my experience almost all of them had the same pattern of lies and excesses.

The physical description of either one usually did not coincide with the impression given through the website and following email correspondence. I was very curious when we knew a couple arriving because the long distance lovers usually had unrealistic expectations about their first meeting. As a result, the initial encounter was a great disappointment. They liked to believe that the fantastic stories they exchanged, prior to their first date, would become a reality. In many instances, these couples had deceived one another with false photographs, either by posting photographs using Photoshop or uploading the photograph of a look-alike. The pattern we saw for years, was that foreign men belittled our young women who, who once they had met the foreign male, became easily disenchanted; they realized that were being told half-truths or that the information had been embellished.

TOM

One of our first experiences of internet encounters was the arrival of Tom; a fifty-year-old American. He taught us a bit about what to expect from this new type of guest. He was shy, kind but to some extent, cheap. We worried because his appearance was careless, which reflected seriously on his figure considering he looked much older than the age he really was.

Tom chose the Inn from the internet, because he wanted a

place where he could feel at home and not feel intimidated during these often awkward rendezvous. He was shy by nature and desperate to see if this new method of meeting people would provide him with a lasting relationship. On the internet he met many "chicks," as he called them, using various websites. Before his trip, Tom booked appointments for the entire first week with several blind dates. He was happy, because he intended to choose at least four candidates from the various women he had contacted through the internet.

From the day he arrived, I hoped it would work for him. Tom had explained that he wanted to start a family as soon as possible, and like many men eager to find a spouse, he was so nervous he could not wait to start the next day and meet those women.

Tom began his visit by paying us in advance for twenty days. His nervousness touched me and I tried to calm him down, but nothing seemed to work. Therefore, the next day I just had to wait to see who was going to show.

The women began to arrive as scheduled, and I became concerned when I saw that they were very young. It was evident by their demeanor and education that these girls were still in high school. The country was in a serious economic depression and jobs were scarce. The war with the guerrillas and drug lords was at the highest peak in our country, and this situation had the economy at a standstill. It was for this reason that there was pessimism amongst many people from all walks of life, and they searched elsewhere for other possibilities. The internet in particular opened several doors, with websites allowing the women to search for a husband from abroad. In addition, Latina brides were in high demand by men from the United States and Europe; and it was a perfect solution for many families who signed up their daughters to find a better life someplace else. However, these girls were about to meet "Don Tom," as they called him. A man that was extremely stingy, despite being a nice but introverted person.

Tom had a ritual for his female guests: as soon they arrived, he would invite them to share a bowl of soup. This surprised everyone, and for many of the women this was too difficult to accept and they decided not to come back. After a few days, Tom did not receive any more visitors. It was known by all of us that these girls expected lavish gifts and invitations, but from Tom they received nothing. Unsuccessfully, I tried to tell him to improve his invite because, what he was offering at the first meeting, didn't work. He didn't believe us and continued with his strategy until the end of his visit. When Tom departed, although frustrated, he assured my employees that he would return.

The second year, the same thing happened. Within a few days, women he found interesting on the internet and, once meeting them, wanted to meet them again, never returned. Furthermore, the few that did show up, once they saw him, blurted out some excuse and left, without giving them the chance to get to know him. I suggested to him that he was probably looking for very young girls and that could be the problem. The women he chose expected more from him. Younger women didn't mind his age but did care for what he had to offer. Tom was meagre with everything that he gave them, and for this reason, Tom was not their ideal candidate. As always, he did not care for my comments.

Fortunately, on Tom's daily trips to a nearby cafe, where

spent his hours writing, he met an amazing male friend. Both of them had many common interests, including writing scripts for movies. Together, they spent their days writing stories of the mafia, drugs, and women. One day, he decided to give me one of the scripts to read and I was appalled by the plot. It portrayed our country in stereotypical fashion, with every Colombian cast as either a drug lord, hit man or sex lord. He was upset about my remarks, but as always, in the end he did not care. Luckily, this hobby entertained him during the remaining days of this visit. The second year stay ended and he left, desiring to return.

During his third year, after few days staying at the Inn, two stunning young women about twenty-five years old and definitely with financial means, began to visit Tom. They came in expensive cars, and were dressed in designer clothes. Both were bilingual.

At first, I was happy to see that finally young women befriended him; but I could not understand how Tom was able to land these girls, after failing with the women who were completely different, from the previous years. There was something about it that concerned me because he was quite naive when it came to relationships. I wanted to know the reason why not one but two girls, clearly attractive, alternated with him keeping him company 24 hours a day. Additionally, these women knew each other and did not appear to have a problem with the arrangement. He would take them out for dinner and stay pretty much the whole day and night with him.

After a few days, I unraveled the mystery. One afternoon, I was in the laundry room counting linens with housekeeping, when I started to hear a conversation in English which filled me with revulsion. One of these "ladies" was explaining to Tom, why her rate was so much higher than the other "lady" as she was giving a grotesque description of her services *in perfect English.* I was glad my housekeeper could not understand a word they were saying, but I needed to stop their conversation before they offended any of my other guests. I stepped out into the corridor, so Tom could understand that I had heard all the discussion taking place between him and that woman. He knew I was bilingual, and I stared at him showing how disgusted I was with what I had heard. They both looked at me, felt uncomfortable, and as soon as they saw I was very upset, they ended their awkward conversation.

A few days later, I had the opportunity to make a remark to Tom concerning his "friend". I explained to him that it was not proper, under any circumstance to have this type of caller because we were a family-oriented Inn, and were not interested in becoming a first-class brothel. We valued the private lives of everyone, and he should also respect the Inn and its rules. I certainly didn't want to see these characters again.

"Don't worry, it will never happen again" he said with great disappointment, clearly embarrassed.

We never saw Don Tom again.

THOMAS

The German tourists were unique because of their stern nature. Thomas, a thirty-year-old gentleman with a career in finance, was very organized and knew exactly what he was going to do. His physique was very attractive, tall and charming. The first day he warned us that he had scheduled three girls to visit: one every hour starting from 10am. The first one arrived fifteen minutes late and although she looked very pretty and nice, Thomas pointed at his watch and told her if she was not going to be on time, he didn't care to have a relationship with her. I urged him to be less precise about the time allotted for the girls to arrive, but he said to me in a commanding tone:

 "Things may work well like this in this country, but in Germany, they do not. Therefore, if a woman wants to marry me this is my first requirement."

The second young woman, by the name of Marcela, showed up only five minutes late, and as he turned to point at the clock, he became mesmerized by her looks. She was a stunning light-skinned African-Colombian, with a cheerful and carefree personality.

Thomas chose Marcela that year, but required her to be meticulously punctual for their next date. She never arrived on time, but Thomas was so smitten by her radiance that he ignored her tardy arrivals. However, he told Marcela that was continuing to look for a spouse and arranged meetings with several other women. Each year he came, he would see other women besides Marcela, until the fourth year, when he only visited her. Before he arrived for the fifth year, Thomas invited her to visit him in Germany. Months later he came for Marcela, and while they were in Germany, decided to marry. A year later, they returned as husband and wife. I was happy for them because really deserved one another, although Thomas was strict in his ways, he was a gentle and noble soul.

110

HELMUT

Thomas' success story with our women lured Helmut, a friend of his. He also wanted to meet *Latinas* because, according to him, German women were too cold and dull. He used the same technique as Thomas, contacting all his dates online.

Helmut quickly whittled his list of potential brides to two possibilities: a very nice woman between thirty-five and forty years old, who worked as a boutique administrator; and the other who was younger girl. Helmut explained that the younger girl was less appealing because she lacked culture and had not pursued a college education; which was very important to our guest.

He was in such rush to find someone that asked me for help. He came to my office and laid two pictures on top of my desk.

"Who would you choose?" he inquired.

When asked that question, I always responded that he should marry the person that could become his soulmate. Additionally, he should bear in mind that this new bride must be able to adapt to his country and customs. He did not answer and left. During a conversation at the end of his stay, Helmut returned to ask:

"Please help me, who would you choose for me?"

"I would pick the boutique administrator because, she seems to be the most appropriate. The other girl is too young for you." I replied.

My response was taking into consideration that Helmut was over 40 years old and needed someone closer to his age; and

111

also this woman seemed friendly, outgoing and carefree. The other girl was barely 20 years old. He considered my response, and without further ADO, he married her.

The couple went to live in Germany and both appeared to be very happy. A year later Helmut called to reserve a room for his wife, who was coming to visit her family. However, she had barely had arrived at the Inn and told us in a nasty way that she had no intention of staying with us. She immediately called a relative, who picked her up shortly afterwards, and whisked her off. We thought it was an unnecessary attitude, but in the end, we didn't know what was really behind all of this.

Unfortunately, a few years later we learned that a Colombian woman was found murdered by her German husband that she had met on the internet. The similarities were frightening, because not only the names matched, but so did their place of residence.

"They're simple coincidences…." we hoped; and I felt bad for this couple's tragic love story in the news, but strongly supposed they were not the couple we knew. Despite our efforts we were unable to find out news from our former guests. Our major concern was that they did not have too much time to get to know each other, and they did rush to get married. Sometimes it is impossible to get to know someone's character, and a relationship could easily end tragically; but we hoped for the best.

United States

From the United States, we had another four guests who arrived looking for brides.

MARK

The first one was Mark; tall with an athletic body, brown eyes, and a friendly smile. His tanned skin made it obvious he liked the outdoors and maintained a healthy lifestyle. He was about to turn 40 years old, with two master's degrees in economics and finance, but never married. After so many years being single, he decided that beginning a family was now his first priority. In the United States he was unable to find anyone suitable; hence, he decided to visit our country to find a *Latina* bride. Although in the past two years, he always stayed at five-star hotels, this time he decided on something less expensive. In his words, the girls he met seemed intimidated by these places, and many did not return.

At the time I was not sure what he meant by it, but when the girls started to visit him, I understood the reason. As had happened to other guests before, the girls he had chosen were coming from less affluent environments. They were usually intimidated because for them, visiting some place expensive was outside their comfort zone. Therefore, their initial behavior was to be reserved and shy; but what struck me most of all was that they all seemed very young. I was surprised that the one to which he was most attracted was a young woman of about 18 years old or less, with long hair and big black eyes, very cute but extremely shy. The first time she arrived Mark spoke to her in his precarious Spanish, and she barely answered him. He invited her to lunch and when she left, Mark asked me a favor:

"Can you please ask her what's wrong?"

The next day, Mark was out and she arrived early. I took the opportunity to reach out to this girl and ask her about Mark. Surprisingly, she opened up and explained to me that she was from a very poor neighborhood in the city, and that her father had registered her on a website of Latin women looking for a husband.

Her name was Maria. She was barely in high school, but considering her main desire was to marry a foreign gentleman to help her family, she didn't care much about finishing her studies. I appreciated her honesty and understood what she was saying because, throughout the years I saw similar situations. On the other hand, I felt sad, considering this girl was more determined to solve her poverty problem without understanding that she could get into more serious problems. Taking into consideration that this young woman had never been anywhere else in the country, nor visited abroad, and in view of her innocence, I asked her a few questions:

"Do you know where the United States is?"

"Do you speak any English?"

"Would you be able to live in another country?"

She didn't answer any of these questions and while we were talking she just stared back at me, emotionless. But, the following question shook her:

"What happens if you want to return because you are unable to adjust living in the States?"

Her face dropped and told me that no-one had made her think about it and she was not sure about the answer. Maria kept nodding her head, but told me point blank, she was still in her quest to find a rich husband, no matter what.

I relayed this conversation to Mark in detail; giving him a clear picture of what had transpired. I explained that this was the situation, not only this young woman, but of many others he was going to meet. I re-emphasized that the most important thing was that his chosen one should be able to adapt to his country. In many instances, the lack of education and culture were going to be a serious challenge for a bi-cultural relationship. It is difficult enough to court someone but more so when the cultural backgrounds are so different. Here they must work, not only on building their relationship, but also on adapting to each other's customs and traditions.

He had an important position in a financial institution and somehow had to choose someone who would be able to mingle, with ease, during formal company events. He did not understand my point of view but appreciated the comments. He continued to see that young girl until the day he had to go home.

Three months later, I received an email from a frustrated Mark. He had managed to talk to Maria again, but she explained that she had decided on another gentleman. I was very sorry to hear this but, having warned him; he chose not to believe me. This young girl was looking for an immediate exit to her poverty. After a few days, Mark sent me an email, in which he explained that he had decided to find a bride in Peru, after taking into consideration his bad experience in Colombia.

ED

The second American was Ed. He had arrived the night before and started his visit with a great impression; he registered as a medical doctor. Furthermore, he was quite attractive, tall, and very blond, was athletic and wore a very well kept mustache. I was happy because he made a nice couple with Carolina, the girl he met on the Internet. But it struck to me that once she met this gentleman, she didn't seem happy. Two days in a row she came to pick him up, without any enthusiasm. As the days continued, she began to avoid the Inn; so we asked Ed what had happened to her. He did not know and was not clear; every day she visited him less and less and they did fewer things together. The second to last day of Ed's visit, Carolina said goodbye to us, giving me the opportunity to talk to her. I was sure something about him disappointed her, but I only said:

"It didn't work out?"

With a sad look, she nodded and responded:

"See you."

Although she didn't say the reason, I was about to find out why.

During his stay, when Ed didn't have much to do, he gave us bottles of natural medicines. These were for different illnesses according to what he had "diagnosed" in us. I began by thinking that this character was quite peculiar, because in order to determine our health, he literally twisted our forearm and diagnosed with "lack of vitamins." Even with my poor knowledge on medicine, I felt that it did not make sense, but I didn't say anything. However, I warned my employees about those pills he had provided to them.

Fortunately, it seemed that the remedies he prescribed involved vitamins and I thought they should not do any harm anyone. However, that night, coincidence or not, I took a tablet from the multivitamins bottle and it gave me a terrible headache. The next day when I saw him, I returned them all; and when I told him what had happened to me, he simply, with concern, mumbled:

"I am sorry."

I proceeded to tell my employees about my own experience.

That afternoon, Ed was standing in the hallway reading, on our bulletin board, an advertisement from the NGO Doctors without Borders. They were looking for volunteers to work in Africa. This organization regularly checked-in and promoted their campaigns, whenever they needed. When Ed finished reading the information, he looked up with longing eyes:

"I would love to be part of this project."

"What prevents you from doing it? It is a sensational organization, and I know some of the doctors who work for them. They are very satisfied with the activities they do. If that's what you want to do, then go ahead!" I urged.

"There's a problem, I'm not a medical doctor" he explained.

I was stunned but tried not to lose my composure. I inquired about why he had registered as a medical doctor, and his answer surprised me even more:

La Posada: short stories from an Inn

"I am a doctor ... but in Oriental Medicine."

This response left me speechless and I thought, what a fraud. He must have read my mind, as he explained:

"I took a course in Oriental medicine for eight months at the Oriental Medicine Institute in New Mexico."

The more explanations made, I felt even more deceived and decided to ask him:

"What is your current profession?"

He boldly said:

"I drive a crane in a warehouse in Colorado."

I quickly understood Carolina's disappointment. I was so upset with his story that I lectured him:

"How is it possible that without being a licensed doctor, you distribute and diagnose diseases when you do not know much about it? You are very irresponsible, because an eight-month course in Oriental Medicine doesn't make you a doctor, here or in your country. Real doctors study for between 12 to 14 years before they can begin their medical practice."

What was odd about the whole situation, is that he didn't say a word; just looked at me and when I finished he left to his room.

Luckily, he departed the next day and hopefully, stopped misleading anyone else.

This was a typical case of someone trying to be more than he really was, but the truth always comes out in the end. Fortunately, the girl he came to meet discovered his exaggerations early on and did not fall into his trap.

JONATHAN

The third American was quite a character. Jonathan was a really big person, who stood six feet tall and according to him, weighed 350 pounds; obvious by all means. His first request was that he needed a bigger bed because ours were too small for him. So, we found a larger bed to accommodate him.

He was proud of his African-American descent and registered as a policeman from the city of Detroit. He went to his room and returned wearing gold necklaces, a hat, and emblems from the Masonic Lodge. For his reasons, it was very important for us to know he was a member of the Lodge. It seemed strange because we understood that the Freemasons are a secretive society; but, if it made him happy, that was his problem.

He met Jenny on the internet and was very excited to meet her in person. She was known to us at the Inn, because every so often Elsa, her sister, provided us with transportation services. During his visit, I took advantage of the fact that we knew Jenny and told her that before committing, she should be certain everything he said was true. I explained to her all the frustrating stories we witnessed in similar circumstances. Nothing helped because she was still very excited about meeting this gentleman. He brought her a lot of gifts, and the truth is, he was genuinely friendly. His visit lasted almost two weeks, and everything went normally. He was generous with her family and enjoyed the entertainments organized in his honor. Despite all of these, I told her sister Elisa about my fears, and she told me that the same thing had happened to her but that we should hope for the best. Six months later, we found out that Jenny had left for Detroit.

Very shortly afterwards I met Elisa and asked about Jenny's life. To my sadness she said:

"Awful! It was all you said; a lot of lies and exaggerations that are making Jenny's life a living hell."

Soon after arriving in the United States, Jenny became pregnant; and having her son was the only thing that kept her in that country but she was suffering from all sorts of difficulties. She was resigned to a life she had voluntarily accepted. All his promises made in Colombia were half-truths and she ended up living in the state of Texas in lousy conditions. The only thing that motivated her was to raise her child. Fortunately, her family in Colombia has always been attentive to provide her with the necessary support if she decides to return at any time.

JOHN

The fourth American was John, a systems engineer, who came to Colombia a few days before he was to get married. John lived in the state of Oregon, on the outskirts of Portland, and had a computer business. He was a charming, kind and generous man. The day after he arrived, he saw us having trouble with our computer, and repaired it at no cost.

Although his final destination was Cali, he believed visiting Bogotá was the most appropriate thing to do. He wanted to visit our country's capital city and immerse himself in our culture, as he thought it was the most appropriate thing to do.

Life had not allowed him to meet the right person yet, and in his late 30s, he wanted more than anything to find the right one. Happily, he had found her on the internet, she was from Cali and her name was Gloria. After two visits to the city and many months of daily conversations by Skype, he felt that Gloria was the love of his life. Several months later, after working on this relationship, he proposed to her. She said yes and they set a date for the wedding.

Gloria told him that preparations for the wedding were ready and it was going to be a lavish event. According to his fiancée, her parents had gone overboard to make it an absolutely fabulous occasion, no expense spared. John was so smitten by this girl that he only wanted it to happen as soon as possible.

His wedding day finally arrived and he radiated happiness. We wished him luck and John took his flight to Cali. This was the first time I was hopeful that a romance born on the internet was going to really work. With this man, so well-grounded and thoughtful, I believed this relationship was going to succeed; and he was more than ready to get married.

But, little did we know it was going to become a terrifying ordeal. To our surprise, he returned a few days later; but in a mysterious way and accompanied by officials from the United States Embassy. They had advised him to stay in a low-profile hotel and to try and not leave the Inn until he was able to fly back home. A few hours before he arrived, we were visited by the embassy employees who decided we were a good option. This turn of events surprised us, because the man we saw leaving to get married was a happy and loving man, and he returned scared and desolated. Fortunately, after resting a little, he told us his story:

When John arrived in Cali, he was welcomed by two men at the airport. He apparently knew they were not relatives but friends of the bride. For this reason, he didn't worry and fearlessly got on their vehicle. Although John had visited Cali before, he was unable to get about anywhere and therefore assumed he was going to his fiancée's house.

However, to his total bewilderment, he was taken to a farm on the outskirts of Cali and, without explanation, they left him locked in a room. He didn't understand anything that was going on, and much less where his fiancée was.

No one spoke to him, and that scared him. The wedding that his fiancée described seemed a nightmare, because she was nowhere to be found and he didn't know why. For reasons he could not understand, these men didn't realize he had a cell phone. John made calls to his office in the United States, and described what just happened to him. He didn't understand the circumstances as to why he was being held at that place; but thanks to his mobile signal, the police located the farm, and three days later John was rescued. The authorities took him to the airport and flew him back to Bogotá on a Drugs Enforcement Administration DEA plane.

We talked with one official from the embassy about the dangers of the internet, where anyone can write anything and make-believe it's true. There was no explanation given about his ordeal, and we didn't ask either. Obviously, it was a serious problem related to drug trafficking, and there was a rumor that John unknowingly fell in love with the daughter of a Cali cartel mobster. He was lucky because this terrible experience could have had a terrible ending. John was too naïve. He did not understand that the type of relationship he had found on the internet was very dangerous.

When he was able to fly back home, I wished him well and hoped that would find the right person elsewhere. Life had given him another chance.

ANA

Although the following story did not relate to stories of encounters on the Internet, it was a case that intrigued everyone at the Inn. Mainly because it was an odd situation and the reservation, done by a woman in Madrid, Spain, was for a peasant woman from our country.

Ana arrived from Barbosa, a town in Santander. She had the appearance of a woman farmer in her late 50's, and functionally illiterate. Her demeanor was typical of someone raised in the countryside; peaceful and humble.

When she registered, we had to fill out her registration as she barely knew how to sign her name, let alone write. Considering she was anxious about being at the Inn, she explained that she had been working for someone in Madrid and that her employer had decided to get her a work visa; but she had to return to Bogotá and apply for it.

When I asked how she ended up in Spain, Ana made a

detailed explanation of her story. In the year 2000, some men from Venezuela came to Barbosa, her hometown, and were looking for people who visited said country during the last year. Ana informed them that she had stayed in San Antonio de Táchira with some relatives, for three months. It classified her to receive the Venezuelan nationality, and a work permit. Therefore, she decided to venture in greener pastures and left for Caracas, where she found a job in the house of her Spanish employer. After a few years and when the political situation in Venezuela deteriorated, the employer decided to return to Madrid with Ana; but before anything else, she was sent back to Colombia, where Ana had to make the arrangements for the work visa at the Spanish Embassy in Colombia.

The next day a very distinguished, tall man, between 35 and 40 years old, came to the Inn, asking for her. When she saw him, they greeted politely and went to the Spanish Embassy. Afterwards, he returned her to the Inn, but not before discussing with Ana, everything she had to say at the Embassy the next day.

At one point, he felt the need to tell me what they were doing. He was of Portuguese origin but lived in Madrid, and was the boyfriend of Ana's employer. For reasons I could not understand, they decided that Ana and him would submit the visa application to the Embassy as bride and groom. I thought this was insane! How could the Embassy believe in this relationship? She was practically an illiterate and didn't fit with that story. Worst of all, is that Ana did not understand the point and somehow, she believed what they were portraying was true. Very excitedly she told me that this man was going to marry her. I couldn't nor had a way to intervene, and didn't know what Ana's future would be; nor did she herself. A few days later, he came to the Inn and told us that everything was arranged, paid her bill and returned Ana to her hometown. We do not know the end of the story but we all hope that everything has gone well for Ana; a hardworking and loyal woman.

Each person in search of love through the internet can succeed, providing there is absolute responsibility and honesty. As technology has opened new opportunities to meet people around the world, it also forces everyone to take great caution. Everyday friendships are possible but to prosper in romantic encounters is more difficult. What some people do not take into account, is that the truth will always come out. It is very sad when it ends in disappointment. Of our stories, it was very sad when they failed, since in the majority of cases they only came to know each other after many months of the anticipated illusion.

La Posada: short stories from an Inn

Good Memories

La Posada

8

La Posada: short stories from an Inn

HAPPY MEMORIES

Although many of the stories I have talked about were close to my heart because of their particular drama, I cannot forget those guests who returned regularly to our Inn and became part of us. Our family atmosphere was a motivating factor for some of them, and although they didn't require much from us, they always left good memories.

Eliza and Juan

Firstly, I remember a very nice and friendly couple, whose demeanor was appealing and they never once showed any kind of problems during their visits. They visited every two months and stayed for a week. This particular case was different because Eliza came from a smaller city, whereas Juan lived in ours. When she was going to arrive, he would personally come to the Inn and make the reservation. Although this couple never told us, they seemed to stay at the hotel with absolute confidentiality. The two of them always showed great excitement towards each other when they arrived, as they seemed deeply in love like youngsters. I always enjoyed seeing them because from the moment they registered, their eyes always had a mischievous glimmer as though they were about to do something extraordinary. They didn't have to say much, to have a great understanding of each. They never showed physical affection, but then, they didn't have to, because what transpired between them was obviously absolute love. When one of them spoke to us, the other one smiled lovingly at the one talking. I was asked by one of our employees if I would dare to ask them when they were going to marry, but I decided it was not necessary. Their bond was so strong, it seemed that they enjoyed their camaraderie and we didn't have to meddle into what appeared to be a perfect relationship.

She was clearly younger and held a prestigious position in a construction company, which he also worked for, but in Bogotá. They were both always thoughtful and well-mannered, making them unforgettable guests during the four years they visited. After arriving back from their long days at work, they would have kind words for our employees. They never asked for anything beyond what we had to offer, and were grateful to all of us during their stay. Juan particularly enjoyed stopping by my office to make comments about Eliza. I remember a time when she arrived looking physically different. Eliza had lost several pounds and looked even younger than before. Juan said to me, very proudly and nodding with a smile:

"I never ask her to make any sacrifices for me, she did it on her own."

But a few weeks later, when I was reading the newspaper, I saw his name in the obituaries. My shock and sadness were overwhelming because he had seemed physically fit. The bizarre part of this story is that I was told a few days later, by one of his good friends that Juan was at work when he had a sudden and fatal heart attack. His friend was a regular in our restaurant and we saw him often. A few days later, I was told by the restaurant manager that this man, who had told me about Juan's untimely death, also suffered a heart attack and died in his office. I was flabbergasted with these two events, and was not surprised that Eliza never returned; there were too many memories of him at the Inn.

La Scala city choir children

Other guests who left good memories, were the kids from the beautiful La Scala city choir. They had to make musical arrangements for a series of songs to be sung at a church ceremony, and because of their young age, the choir director decided it was easier to accommodate them in the same place during their four-day stay. Although they had a hard time managing the boisterous energy of these youngsters, during the mornings they divided the group into the different voices, and in the evenings, the choir sang what they learned.

Best of all, our neighbors were so happy with our guests that they asked if the choir could present them a concert; an idea welcomed by the choir Director. The last day in the inner patio of our Inn the entire choir sang a beautiful musical repertoire that they had learned in the past few days. It was quite a spectacle and exciting for our neighbors. I looked around the patio and was grateful, because my next-door-neighbors were, for an hour, absorbed and listening at their windows to those voices that seemed to come from angels. In addition, we felt very privileged because later on that year this choir competed at the Chorus Festival in Beijing and returned, bringing several awards to our country.

Mister Masiello

Another guest, who was appreciated by the entire staff, was Mister Masiello; an Italian man, who came for a month every year. He was an elderly person, always very well dressed and groomed. He always requested a room with a shared bathroom, which we appreciated since they were the least desired rooms. His visits filled us with gifts, but what I appreciated the most, was that he was always considerate to all the employees at the Inn. He would have long conversations with them and would take the time to help them through his multiple connections as he considered they were worth the time. He advised many members of our staff by finding solutions to their banking problems that they had been unable to find. He seemed to know people in the highest positions of the financial world in this city. It seemed that his purpose, was that everyone he knew, was doing well; otherwise he would find a way to help, every which way he could. We never knew what brought him to this city, as his time at the Inn passed quietly. On occasions when he went out, he did not seem to have urgency for anything.

Suddenly, he would announce that it was time to depart, and it brought a sadness to all of us because, in a sense, we all felt like we were being taken care by him. His Italian demeanor was like that of a godfather and we very much appreciated it. He kept his personal life private and during the five years he stayed with us, he never showed up at the Inn with anyone different with the exception of a couple that seemed to be good friends. After the fifth year, he didn't return and we never knew why. We tried to find out through the people he knew but they also had the same concern, because nobody seemed to get news from him. Eventually, with much regret and sadness, we learned that he died in his country because of a heart attack.

Two Japanese sisters

I also remember with affection, the two Japanese sisters who were Colombians at heart. They came to stay regularly but at separate times, because each worked for different non-governmental organizations. They always arrived within a week's difference. The amazing thing was that although they were not twins, they were identical and had the same tastes. Despite the fact that we always confused them, they never showed displeasure; just politely corrected us. Unfortunately, after four years they could not return because they decided to put family first. They both had small children and being close to them was their priority.

American Family

Others we remember fondly was that American family who came from the state of Montana in the United States. The father, a Colombian national, immigrated to the United States when he had a terrible disagreement with his family. He left Colombia at a very young age to venture away from them, and ended up living in a State known for its incredible green prairies and sparsely populated towns on the border with Canada. He chose Montana to study and get married because its high mountains and green valleys reminded him of Colombia. As time passed by, his teenage daughters began to ask him questions about his birthplace. He decided then to take them for a visit and give his country a chance. Deep down he always dreamed of reconciling with his family and homeland, even though he was a little worried about how well they would be received.

They spent a very happy month and a half with us, but a few days before they had to return home he had a terrible scare. That day they purchased a famous roasted chicken, and when they arrived at the Inn they went straight to their room. Less than half an hour later, they came downstairs with the youngest daughter, who was turning blue. She had eaten a piece of chicken and unknowingly swallowed a bone; they did not know what to do. Without wasting any time, I sent them in my car to an emergency room in a nearby clinic. The most amazing thing was that the doctor who attended her, could not believe that this young woman ate a bone the size of a little finger. Fortunately, all the procedures were successful and she could quickly return to her family. The father never stopped thanking us for having assisted them in such a distressing time. It was the least we could do, as we wanted that this terrible ordeal not to be their memory of our city. In our minds at the Inn, we wanted them to go back to Montana, looking forward to coming back again.

Despite that our country was under severe problems with the guerillas, the father achieved his purpose; showing his family the friendly face of Colombia. Furthermore, he reconciled with everyone and everything that caused him, as he explained, much bitterness. Everyone left happy and eager to return.

BAD MEMORIES

A Soccer team

There was something naive on our part when it came to some guests; often coming from abroad and sometimes left without paying or took things from the Inn. We learnt that taking things, like the towels, are well-known souvenirs for frequent travelers. During a one-night stopover of a soccer team from South America, we lost 11 towels. Fortunately, we were able to stop this problem as a housekeeper, from the Weston Hotel in Miami, who stayed with us for several days gave us hints and tips about what to do in this circumstance.

Ann

But the case that provoked us the most impact was a young woman, who arrived to do research in various libraries in the capital. Ann was studying Hispanic History in a graduate program at the University of London. Her three months' stay was dedicated to study many authors of that genre at our national library. We saw her leave every morning with her tote bag and a Notepad; which, when she returned in the afternoon, Ann always took out on the living room table and spent time making a summary of her daily work. She was very thorough and committed to her studies from Monday to Saturday. On Sunday, she dedicated it to rest and usually stayed in the room reading a book, or visiting with other guests. Sometimes she went out sightseeing around the city with other guests but always returned to the Inn early.

The day came when she had to return to London. I remember it with great detail, because it was a Sunday and I received a call from the Alejandro, our associate manager. He informed me that Ann was traveling early on Monday but, the moment she started to pack her things, realized her laptop disappeared from her room. According to her, the thief only left the sleeve for her laptop. It was our first burglary and I could not understand the details he was giving me over the phone.

Despite being my day off, I went to the Inn immediately, to learn more information about the theft. From the very first moment I received the call I had doubts, which increased once I reached the Inn. Before talking to Ann, I was reminded of the fact that, evidently during the three months she stayed with us, no one had seen said laptop. I asked her where she stored it and why no one had seen it, but she insisted that it had been stolen and showed us a cover from a well-known brand. Throughout this predicament, it was strange because Ann did not lose composure and kept reminding us that the equipment was insured, and showed us the insurance policy.

According to this insurance certificate, the laptop was worth four thousand dollars. The thought of having to pay such sum made me sick, as it would be at least our earnings of ten guests coming in during eight days. With a calmness Ann told me:

"Don't worry. I won't charge you for the laptop. The only thing I need is to be taken to the police station to make a report on the burglary. I have it insured and it is not a problem."

Therefore, I volunteered to take her, and we drove to the nearest police station to file the complaint.

In the proceedings, I had to translate what she said to the police sergeant. At the end of the statement, the police officer turned to me, taking advantage that Ann did not speak or understand Spanish, he asked me:

"Did you see the computer at any time?"

I shook my head, no. He confirmed what we were thinking. Often foreigners do not travel with their laptops but take out insurance on their computers before a trip. When they return to their countries, they file the respective complaint and charge insurance companies for the "lost" computer, getting a new replacement. According to the police, our country is often used to commit this type of fraud and he told me there were times when he received up to four reports a week from foreign tourists claiming theft.

Once the complaint report was completed, we returned to the car and I think that Ann found me more thoughtful than normal, because she asked me if there was something wrong. To which I replied briefly with a no, but very much wanted to tell her my real feelings about this ordeal, yet I decided it was not appropriate at the time.

This woman was going to show us as a country of thieves to a British Insurance company, when she was the only person responsible for it. However, there was no way we could prove this fraud. Ann paid the balance of her bill at the Inn without asking us for any money; something that gave me an absolute mistrust in her, and I was glad when she left the next day. There was never a claim from her or any news related to this event, but we were glad it ended without us having to pay for something that never existed. We definitely gained in experience, vowed to end this type of scam.

Employee from an international organization

Two years later, an employee from an international organization registered at the Inn and he only had one bag with him. While he was at the front desk his bag was never out of his sight. He went to his room, but a short while later, he returned very quickly, claiming that someone had stolen his laptop. Fortunately, we knew this trick and calmly asked him to prove that there had been a laptop in that bag. We asked him, how could someone steal his laptop, if he had the bag with him at all times? Although he left the front desk angry, he did not discuss this anymore. This man only stayed one night, but that was good enough for us. We well remembered our first laptop fraud, and we were not about to accept another.

UGLY MEMORIES

Hugo

We cannot stop thinking about a guest who arrived one night in a sorry state; Hugo. He could not stand up due to the high level of alcohol in his body. A friend of his brought him to the Inn because he had been thrown out from the house, and he was told that until he recovered from that addiction, he couldn't go home. We were perplexed as he was well dressed and looked as someone used to the good life.

Days later, he told us how he had wasted his life because of his drinking problem. He lost everything he had, and went from being the owner of a sumptuous apartment, brand cars and other luxuries, to having absolutely nothing. Hugo was a first line expert in finance but due to his addiction, he unfortunately lost more than one chance of having a brilliant career. When he was sober, he was kind and polite, but when he was drunk he was unbearable.

On several occasions, I spoke to him asking to curb his

behavior with others, but my plea didn't work because he could care less about the other guests.

I paid my dues for being complacent with him, and tried not to be bothered by his continuous antics. In a way, I felt he needed us more than we needed him, because he was very difficult to handle.

Until one night; an incident with the night receptionist, Jose, was the conclusion to five months of scandals. Jose did not give him his room key because he was boisterous, demanding and absolutely drunk. I had warned him in advance that we were not going to allow him inebriated. But, at 11 pm, after hitting Jose, he forced his way into his room and broke everything in his path, including the door. When I arrived at the Inn, 15 minutes later; I found that disaster. I told him he that could sleep in the room that night, but should vacate it the next day. I personally, wasn't able to throw him out on the street, because it was clear that at that time of the night, he had nowhere to go. Peculiarly and despite his level of intoxication, he understood everything and apologized.

When I arrived the next day, he had paid his account and left.

The worst thing is that I found him several months later on the street. Hugo did not have to say anything because the smell of alcohol was indisputable. Sadly, I saw he had missed the opportunity to recover, and I did not see anything that showed his intention to do so. Therefore, I wished him luck and hoped he would find someone who would motivate him to end this addiction because, for him, time was running out.

La Posada: short stories from an Inn

Mark

Another challenging situation that unfolded before our eyes, without giving us the possibility of doing much until the end, was a particular event that took place when an exchange student from Brazil arrived to stay at our Inn for six months. Mark was a young man in his early 20's, with blue eyes, blonde hair, freckled faced and from the start, he announced he was gay. He was adorable and in his behavior he was very discrete. He quickly adapted to his routine, and it only took him a few days to find friends. He was very happy with us, the college and the city.

One day he mentioned that his boyfriend was coming to visit him for a couple of weeks, from Brazil. I was surprised because, from the beginning of his stay, he seemed to have found company in a young man from Colombia, called Jose. In their short relationship, they were inseparable and seemed to be very happy together. I was obviously glad he was going to have a visitor from home, but a bit nervous, because I was not sure how he was going to handle his boyfriend and the new acquaintance.

After a few days, his boyfriend George arrived and left us all in shock. Standing before us was clearly a man 40 years older. He was courteous and educated, but seemed bad tempered all the time. Mark was very busy with his school hours and schedule, and this caused daily arguments between them.

George spent his hours reading and watching television, while Mark attended his classes. George did not utter a word unless he was spoken to, and nobody wanted to have anything to do with him because he seemed angry all the time.

One day, Mark walked into my office and told me that they had, had an ugly disagreement relating to their relationship and both decided to break up. Mark explained that George was staying for a few more weeks in his room, and therefore, each one would continue with their daily routine without any changes; Mark going to school and coming in late, and George staying at the Inn all day.

However, a few days later, I received a call from our night receptionist, Hector, at 11:30 pm. Hector was not able to speak properly, he seemed to be in some kind of shock and required my presence at the Inn as soon as possible. Although I tried not to panic, I was afraid that someone had broken in and burglarized the Inn. Never in the years had we worked together, had I heard Hector so scared. Being so late at night, my father decided to accompany me considering the situation could turn ugly. He was a retired engineer from Harvard, very religious and a family man; besides which, he was working as a volunteer in the army reserves, so his help could be important. It never crossed my mind, that I was going to encounter anything different to a break-in, and not to the deplorable event that transpired.

Although it took only ten minutes for us to arrive, I was startled by the situation I was going to encounter. As I parked the car, the door of the inn opened and Hector came out pale and dumbfounded. This was a 350 pound very tall man, with beautiful blue eyes and the demeanor of someone brought up on a farm. His behavior with the guests was educated and respectful, to the point that someone described him as a huge teddy bear.

When I asked him what happened, it took him some minutes to gain composure, before he explained the incident that caused his great concern and to me great disgust and anger. He described the reason why he needed me so urgently, and at that point I did not understand why he felt ashamed. I was sorry that my father had to hear this episode because in his wildest dreams, he never thought something like this would happen around us. I turned to look at him and he was absolutely speechless.

According to Hector: George was watching television in the living room as always, and, with the exception of Mark, all the other guests were in their rooms. Hector decided to sit down on another couch to watch the TV program too. He confessed to me that he fell asleep but something awoke him up suddenly. George had climbed on top of him and started to kiss and grope him in places he did not dare to tell me. Fortunately, Hector's physique helped him out and he was able to push this man off him and onto the floor. George very quickly stood up and left to go to his room, limping. Hector was so shaken by this attack that took him a while before he reached the phone to call me. He could not understand the reason for this, and what I found endearing was the fact that Hector was scared that he might have hurt our guest. Although I reassured him that George was probably fine, my first reaction was to calm him down, and I said to him:

"With those beautiful eyes, who wouldn't want you?"

It brought a smile, and he was grateful that his actions would not bring him trouble. I told him that George was the one who behaved badly and I immediately wrote a note asking this unwanted guest to check out the following day. Our Inn was family oriented and was not about to accept situations such as the one described; it would give us a terrible reputation.

My father never commented on this episode, but he did tell the rest of the family how proud he was that I had handled this episode professionally and flawlessly.

George walked into my office the next day and apologized. Although I accepted his apology, I did not allow him to stay another day with us. When Mark heard the news, he was ashamed of his friend; I told him it that it did not reflect badly on him at all.

Throughout the years, we respected every guest staying with us, but I drew the line when something like this transpired. Mark stayed with us for the complete term. When he left, he left us smiling and thanking us for our hospitality; something we cherished coming from him.

La Posada: short stories from an Inn

Lessons we Learned

La Posada

9

La Posada: short stories from an Inn

Since we began our work at the Inn, we knew that its location in a residential area could lead to problems at night. In order to preserve the tranquility for the neighboring residents, we committed to not allowing excessive noise nor having guests extending their exuberance into the streets. It is well known in Latin America to finish parties or events on the street, hence disturbing the neighbors. We also had to watch out for our own night personnel so that they did not take advantage of their position; for example, renting out rooms for people checking-in late and pocketing the cash for themselves. For this reason, we established a number of strategies to control this known abuse of position, and believed, naively, that we had achieved it.

CAMILO

After reviewing the inn's activities at night, we discovered that our night receptionist had established his own lucrative business and for that reason, we let him go. Fortunately, we recruited someone who should have been the perfect candidate: Camilo, a theology student, studying at a very prestigious University. Everything seemed to be under control; Camilo was a kind person and very attentive. His presence exuded respect; a very tall man with a stylish manner. But, after a few months, at a time when the Inn began to receive more visitors, I continually received complaints about his behavior. As the first grievance was from a group of athletes, I decided to pay special attention to what they said.

Camilo had decided to watch over the girls; not allowing them to be in their male teammates rooms and vice versa. He would knock on the door when he suspected someone was seeing another team member. He explained that everybody had to be in the right room. Countless times I had conversations with him regarding invading the privacy of our guests, and how we could not do this anymore. But, despite my requests, he, amazingly, continued to meddle in the lives of our guests. He seemed to be on a mission to save them all and that caused frustration for more than one guest.

I was not sure how to handle the issue until something happened that was the last straw. I was in the process of taking care of the bill of a frequent traveler from the States, and as he was checking out, I asked him a number of questions about services. He kindly explained that everything was good, but that we should compel the employee, who opened the door at night, to wear a uniform. I looked at him puzzled, and said:

"He has a uniform."

To which he replied:

"Well then I don't know, because he opens the front door in his pajamas."

I was so astonished by this information that I was unable to register what my guest was telling me. It was so absurd and I was left speechless. But the worst thing was that, although it was absurd, I wanted to laugh because I could not understand how a person, that I believed to be educated, could behave so unprofessionally.

But, when I confronted Camilo about this new situation, and explained that he should comply with the uniform code; he came up with the most outrageous answer. He looked terrified and said to me:

"But you must understand that after 10 pm, I must wear my pajamas so that I am ready to go to bed".

Such was my surprise to such an absurd response because, this was the man in charge of the night shift: someone who had to take care of the inn from 7pm until 7am. Therefore, I had no choice but to put an end to his contract. There were already too many complaints about him, and we could not continue to have an unprofessional night manager; something that was critical for the proper running of the Inn. A lesson that never was forgotten.

HOUSEKEEPING

Another experience we learned was that as we pursued to provide the best service possible, we often overlooked training our employees as to how the service should be provided. This particular instance was related to the additional services we offered. Although my next lesson was the most expensive yet, we were grateful because it ended well.

One Tuesday, as soon as I arrived, the front desk immediately advised me that we had received a complaint from one guest. The Inn had been opened for less than a year and unfortunately, we were still learning about its management.

According to the complaint, the housekeeping had cleaned a wool suit for the guest and ruined it. I went to see the housekeeper in charge of the floor the guest was staying on, and asked her to retrieve the suit and clean it again. But

149

around noon time, when the guest returned he said that he was not pleased with the service provided. Therefore, I asked to see the garments because I wanted to know what the real problem was. When the housekeeper showed up with the suit, I was left stunned and astonished for several minutes; the suit had shrunk at least four sizes and the wool fabric was clearly damaged. We were frustrated, because we had been in business for less than a year and were not financially prepared to compensate this guest. But, we had to repair the damage, before the problem worsened and we experienced added consequences. This particular guest was a member of the coffee growers group and stayed with us often; therefore, we should resolve the complaint because we accepted it was our mistake.

When Blanca, the housekeeper agreed to clean the garment, she simply used the washer and dryer, rather than sending the suit to the cleaners. Errors should be paid but the most important thing was that we had to earn the trust of our guest again. Fortunately, he appreciated our response, because we bought a gift card from a famous men store and gave it to him with our apologies. For years afterwards, he remained to be a regular guest of our inn.

THE SHAMAN

Although many situations gave us satisfaction and enjoyment, during some situations we despaired. One in particular caused us much concern. On occasions we needed to be alert to the strange situations when they happened; especially, after an instance that left us without much to do. The events at the Inn unfolded as follows:

We had an incredible end of the year, as we had full occupation during November, December, and the first days of January. Suddenly, our bookings abrupt halted. The phones stopped ringing, and reservations went down to zero. Every day, I checked on the internet but there was nothing, it was as if from one minute to the next we ceased to exist. This was very difficult to understand.

After fifteen days and there was no one staying at the Inn, I started to think we had been cursed. That afternoon, I conveyed my thoughts to the staff and how this was a strange situation considering we couldn't find any explanation. Although I tried not think about it because is a very sensitive topic, I commented that it was as if we were somehow under a spell.

It is not unusual in Latin America; black magic has been used for centuries in cases of vengeance. It is very common, particularly, in the lower socioeconomic levels, where people practice black magic when they feel betrayed or upset with someone or something. For this reason, it was not a surprise to my employees that there was a possibility that someone had used black magic against the Inn. However, none of us could recollect anyone who could be so upset with us.

Discreetly, Ricardo, one of my staff, originally from a town near the Amazon jungle, told me a shaman from his hometown, who by chance was in our city, could come to the Inn. According to locals, a shaman is a person who is described as having access and ability to influence the spirits. They have special rituals, enter into a trance state, and can determine if there are strange damaging energies.

Although I had reservations with having anything to do with

this type of person, I also was at the point of not having no other options. Ricardo seemed very confident that this man could help us. Although these shamans or witch doctors are often used by people in our country, I was at crossroads in this entire situation. What I wanted is someone to clearly tell us what was going on. After thinking it for a while, I decided that, on behalf of my staff who were pretty concerned about it, I would pay this man and hope for the best.

The next day the shaman arrived. My initial thoughts were that this man looked bizarre and this worried me a bit. He seemed to have no use for a hair brush, and his clothes were barely adequate. Although he exuded absolute self-confidence, his expression was cold and distant; and it seemed that his eyes looked through us. It was definitely eerie. But what struck me the most, was that he literally walked around sniffing all over the place. He did not say a word and walked behind Ricardo, who guided him all through the Inn. No room nor space was left out from his observing eyes. At one point, the shaman left the Inn's quarters because he couldn't find anything out of order. However, when he and Ricardo entered the Inner patio, and had not taken more than fifteen steps, he stopped, paralyzed in front of a flower pot that was more dead than alive. The shaman immediately turned around and told us:

"This is the problem! You must get rid of this at once."

We were shocked! From the fifteen flower pots on the Inner patio, he chose the only plant that was not ours. Furthermore, it was left by someone who didn't work for us anymore, and she had told us that she would remove it at a later date.

For that reason and at the insistence of the shaman, it was immediately removed from the premises and put on the street, from where we hoped the garbage truck would pick it up soon. According to the shaman it was filled with soil from the cemetery and other things we didn't want to know about. Afterwards, I did have to reimburse the pot owner but I didn't care because it was absolutely worth it. A few days later, we were back in business and working as normal.

We were fascinated by the whole ordeal but decided not to delve into the subject in more depth; we moved forward and did not look back. A working environment with bad energy, hatred, and evil is not a good place and we had managed to get rid of it. Although it was quite a strange experience, we hoped that we will not have to deal with something like that ever again.

A FINAL LESSON

Despite the fact that we would never see the central characters of these stories again, we will remember them forever. We cherished every minute of each story and remember them as if it were yesterday. These stories left an indelible mark on us.

In many of the instances, we learned lessons of courage, tolerance, friendship and hope; and we also suffered for those who took terrible decisions and we were unable to help them further.

We cherished those guests who allowed us to be part of their lives. Our desire to help them in every way we could, was genuine and I know we always did our best. I hope they felt the same.

Our work at the Inn allowed us to have an interesting view into other people's lives and build relationships, but it was also evident that the day arrived, when they had to leave.

ABOUT THE AUTHOR
MARIA EMILIA ORTEGA-SAMPER

When I was twelve years old, I was disheartened that a poor neighborhood, up the mountains, had a schoolhouse in terrible condition and had no teacher. My parents and a group of neighbors decided to work on rebuilding the school house, and with the help of the city; finding teachers. This was successfully accomplished two and half years later. In the meantime, I spent my Saturday mornings teaching these kids how to read and write. A job I continued to do until graduating from high school. Growing up in a family, where we were taught to think that helping others, whenever it was possible, was the right thing to do.

Therefore, following this experience I chose teacher training for my college education. But, during a trip to Mexico City, I was amazed at a sports center for kids, where the children enjoyed their experiences and left with a smile on their faces. This defined my graduate choice and I select to study Human Movement for my Master's and Doctorate Degrees at Boston University.

Upon my return, I worked, at national level, for the Sports Agency, and with various sports associations. What really attracted me was working with the athletes. However, getting an appointment to work with the athletes were based on government politics; hence, I decided to pursue a career in sports marketing. At the time, it had become a new trend; and although it was a great experience, I missed not having to work with people. After several years of working in sports marketing; when the owners of a new Inn, still under construction, offered me the job to manage it, I took this challenge as my own.

It started as a newly launched B&B in a beautiful setting, and seven and a half years later, I passed them back a property with a good reputation in the B&B world. An amazing experience, where I was always trying to do my best to help the people I met from all over the world and from all walks of life.

ABOUT
PENCRAFT PUBLISHING

At PenCraft Books (PCB) we know what it's like to have a dream of being a published author. Individually, we have been through the publishing process. It isn't easy and the entire process from writing to having books sold requires a huge learning curve.

At PCB we're committed to taking the stress out of having to know everything from editing to publishing to marketing. This means our authors are free to do what they do best and write. Consequently, we mentor writers through the visioning and goal setting process. Essentially, we help them become authors and achieve a finished manuscript. We work hand-in-hand with our authors, guiding them through the entire process to help them succeed.

We also format finished manuscripts so they're available for readers both physically in bookstores, and on-line for our Kindle readers. Following which, we mentor our authors in the marketing of their published work to reach the widest possible audience.

We recognise that there are a lot of choices out there for publishing services. That's why PCB researched what authors really want and actually need. It's also the reason why we offer a tailored approach.

Our research consistently said that writers *wished they'd had a personal mentor when they first started writing*. Someone who cared and had the expertise to guide them along the path from original idea; to beating the dreaded procrastination, which is really about overcoming limiting self-beliefs and where our writing coaches come in handy; right through to seeing their work in print.

However, the journey doesn't end there as most authors think it does. It's said that *writing a book is the easy part; it's the marketing of it when the real work starts.* That's why PCB also helps its authors stand out in a crowded market place with a marketing strategy to reach the widest possible audience and achieve maximum sales.

Our expertise enables us to provide support to new writers going through every tough spot imaginable, to just being there for the more experienced authors.

www.PenCraftPublishing.com

31007864R00096

Made in the USA
Columbia, SC
31 October 2018